March 1970

The Legacy of Tom Dooley

To Gary Tom

In deep appreciation

for your help and

guidance —

Verne Chaney

Also by Lawrence Elliott

JOURNEY TO WASHINGTON
with Senator Daniel K. Inouye

ON THE EDGE OF NOWHERE
with James Huntington

GEORGE WASHINGTON CARVER: THE MAN WHO OVERCAME

A LITTLE GIRL'S GIFT

The Legacy of
Tom Dooley

by
Lawrence Elliott

THE WORLD PUBLISHING COMPANY
NEW YORK AND CLEVELAND

The author gratefully acknowledges permission
to reprint lines from "Stopping by Woods on a
Snowy Evening" from *Complete Poems of Robert Frost.*
Copyright 1923 by Holt, Rinehart and Winston, Inc.
Copyright 1951 by Robert Frost. Reprinted by
permission of Holt, Rinehart and Winston, Inc.

Published by The World Publishing Company
2231 West 110th Street, Cleveland, Ohio 44102
Published simultaneously in Canada by
Nelson, Foster & Scott Ltd.

Second printing—August, 1969

Manufactured at World Publishing Press,
a division of The World Publishing Company,
Cleveland, Ohio.

Library of Congress Catalog Card Number: 69-19310

PRINTED IN THE UNITED STATES OF AMERICA

WORLD PUBLISHING
TIMES MIRROR

This book is dedicated to

Sophie Dundy

The Splendid Americans

These are the Thomas A. Dooley Foundation volunteers who have served overseas since its inception.

Mildred Adams
Margaret Alberding
Lynn Allen, R.N.
Rene Allen, R.T.
Margaret Allurding, R.N.
Judy Angove, M.T.
Eric Anders, M.D.
Kathy Anderson
Martha Zipfel-Atuk
Richard Baldwin, M.D.
Marion Uhalt-Barker
Elizabeth Bassford
Kay Billings
Richard Blanchfield
Barbara Boyd
Sharon Boyd
Maurice Brazean, M.D.
Gail Brenkey, R.N.
Diane Brown
Lauren Brown
Jelena Brunetti
Eleanor Buckley
Ann Burton
Joan Butler, R.N.
Mary Frances Butler
Sherry Campbell
Ann Cannon
Katherine Cantwell
Sister Carlotta, R.N.
Judith Chodat-Carlson
Juliet Carlson
Jose Castellanos, M.D.
Janice Castle
Patricia Cherpes
Ann Cohen

Beverly Faye Cohen, R.N.
Carol Collins
Monica Conley
Corinne Connor
Dr. & Mrs. Robert Conway
Rose Craft
Maureen Daly
Olivia Beth Daniell
Mary Davia, M.D.
Mr. & Mrs. Jack Davis
Frances Day
Alex DelCarmen, M.D.
Katherine Streb-Delk
Judy Derenthal
Lie DeVocht
Doris Dieter
James Dineen, M.D.
Mr. & Mrs. Robert Dishong
Donna Doherty
Georgia Drakes
Marge Dunlap
Annette Duvall
John Duyn
Carol A. Dyall
Shirley Robinson-Ellgaard
Rita Fabac
Maria Tuboly-Faxander
Jennifer Fenn, R.N.
G. Tim Ford
Meredith Fortune
Dolores Frank
Karin Freytag
Joan Gale

Marlene Geiser
Vernell Geistweidt, R.N.
Creagh Gemmell, R.N.
Patricia Gibbon
Ann Gilmartin, R.N.
Marilyn Giroux
Seyem Gizatullin
Sally Glaze
Gail Goodson
Reginald Gordon
Charlene Graben
Ann Green
Geraldine K. Gross
Rose Marie Grozak, R.N.
Albert Harris
Ute Ruhland-Harris
Holly Hetzer
Christine Hill, R.N.
Mr. & Mrs. Jack Hjelt
Carol Hodson
James Hooper, M.T.
Keye Hollister
Patricia Horan
Pauline Kastre-Hubic
Wendy Huggins
Carol Wilkinson-Humphrey
Susan Huxtable
Joan Hvezda
Mary Ianziti, R.N.
Kathleen Ison
Waldo Jones, M.D.
Violet Juodakis, M.D.
Dorothy Justice
Steve Kaplan

Phyllis Keegan
Ruth Ann Keilman
Ann Kidder, R.N.
Judith Kinnear
Vera Klein
Sonja Kleven
Mary Weinlader-
Knutsen
Barbara Koplow
Miriam Kuhlman
Joan Lampert
Sue Lapidus
Rosemarie Lenel, M.D.
Diane Lewis, M.T.
Marilyn Lewis
Irene Liddy
Renda Lindley
Dolores Linnenbrink
Judson Lloyd, M.D.
Elizabeth Louis
Nancy Lynch, R.N.
Alice McCabe
Kathy McClay
Carrie deRossett-
McCoy
Carolyne McCue, M.T.
Tessa McDonnell
Wayne McKinny, M.D.
Shirley McManus
Mae Mercereau
Kay Miller
Emillee Millsap
Marleane Thompson-
Mitchell
Richard Mitchell, M.T.
Barbara Moore
Phyllis Morita, M.T.
Anne Moroziuk
Jan Elster-Muenze
Geraldine Murphy
Robert Murphy
Caroline Murray

Fernando Navales, M.D.
Patricia O'Hara
Zara Ormerod
Pat Ott, R.T.
Everett Owens
Roswitha Gotte-Paley
Robert Parshall
Margaret Patipatana-
koon, M.D.
Arlene Perritt
Frank Placas
Lois Pritchard
Mr. & Mrs. Peter Purdy
Shirley Turner-Rafael
Jerry Rand
Shirley Hesselroth-
Rector
Dr. & Mrs. Carl
Redderson
Theodore Reich, M.D.
Jovita Rivella
Florentino Rosario,
M.D.
Peter Rout
Mr. & Mrs. Peyton
Rowan
Kathy Ryan
Nancy Ryback
Stella Saint
Barbara Schnepp
Donna Scodes
Barrett K. Seeley, M.T.
Loren Senseman, M.T.
Sharon Sensenbaugh
Narayn K. Shah
Sandra Miller-Shugert
Virginia Singleton, M.D.
Rebecca Slaton
Lee Slatter
Pat Slattery
Alta Mae Smith
Gwen Smith

Mary Martha Smith
Virginia Keibler-Smith
Diane Snuff
Virginia Souders, M.T.
Evelyn Spoor
Mr. & Mrs. David
Stanley
Dawna Stearman
Dora Lynn Stokes, M.T.
Judith Stover
Sharon Tjugum-
Swildens
Heidi Tartaretti
Anita Taylor
Jennifer Thomas
Stephen Thorngate,
M.D.
Juanita Tiffany, R.N.
Nancy Tough
Shirley Turner
Martha Vilander, R.N.
Nancy Vogel, M.T.
Christrose von
Schoening
Jean Wagers
Dan Walker
Linda Waller
Penny Watson
Zola Watson, R.N.
Barbara Wells, R.T.
Carl Weidermann, M.D.
Jane Wershay
Margrit Wey
Sheila Weygman, R.N.
Sheila White
Beth Wilkins
Margaret Wilson
Patricia Wood
Marlene Normandin-
Woodworth

I am grateful to these brave men and women who, having lived the experiences described in this book, were willing to share them with me. I should like to express my appreciation, too, to the editors of the *Reader's Digest* who had faith in this project and who helped me realize it.

Lawrence Elliott
Paris
December 3, 1968

Contents

Foreword by Malcolm W. Dooley   xi

    I. Chaney   1

   II. On the Other Side of Greenwich Village   29

  III. Quang Ngai   77

  IV. Ban Houei Sai   107

   V. Khong Island   137

  VI. What Can One Person Do?   165

 VII. The Purdys   183

VIII. The Splendid Americans   203

  IX. To Sail a Dark River   227

Illustrations following page 112

Foreword

I HAVE SIX children and my brother Tom never had any, and I used to tease him about being a bachelor and all the "joys of fatherhood" he was missing. Then one day, perhaps when I'd been laying it on a little thick, Tom said, "I know how you feel about your kids, Malc. I've got a whole kingdom of them."

And it was true. Tom Dooley's family consisted of all the sick and scared and underfed kids of Southeast Asia, and he loved them and worked as hard to bring a little light and comfort to their lives as any natural father ever worked to provide for his own brood. They had become his personal responsibility and he couldn't forget it.

Not even when he was dying. I sat by his bed three days before the end and he said to me, "Malcolm, if my kingdom of kids is forgotten, I will not have lived at all. Don't let people forget."

I walked outside Memorial Hospital in New York those snowy January days in 1961 and I wondered what I could do. You will see in this book how Tom was the heart and soul and life force of the medical relief operations he had introduced to Vietnam and Laos and Cambodia and how, when all of us who worked with him knew that he had to die of that melanoma in his chest, it simply did not seem possible that any other man could take his place. What, then, would happen to his jungle hospitals? Where would the money come from to support the field clinics, and where the fiery inspiration to attract the doctors and nurses who staffed them and brought hope to lands that had only known despair.

And of course the answer was that no other man did take Tom's place—but his work is carried on by a whole host of men and women who were moved by his message: that those who can—individuals, not governments—must help those who are so far lost in history's backwaters. And that is what this book is about, the splendid Americans who have picked up the burden so reluctantly laid down by Tom Dooley.

Ambassador Henry Cabot Lodge once said, "The work which Dr. Dooley has done has struck a loud responsive chord among Americans. He has appealed to what Lincoln called 'the better angels of our nature'—our compassion and generous concern for our fellow man."

I believe this to be Tom's greatest gift to America and the world. He said, "I am convinced that our nation is founded on a principle that ordinary men will accomplish extraordinary things." And when he was dead, ordinary men, men who, alone, would never have presumed to assume Tom Dooley's mission assumed it anyway and, refusing to fail, succeeded.

You will get to know them in Larry Elliott's moving story of their work, the dangers and difficulties they faced, and the incredible difference they made, this handful, to the lives of millions of people. There is Verne Chaney, who gave up a flourishing medical practice because he was almost mystically certain that there had to be a

Thomas A. Dooley Foundation. There is Carl Wiedermann, who worked to the very limits of his endurance
"in that sea of misery" and, in the end, was swallowed
by it. There is Al Harris, a self-conscious young corpsman
who didn't believe in himself—until he realized there was
no one else to do the jobs that needed doing in Quang
Ngai and Ban Houei Sai. There is Dr. Mary Davia, who is
still there, and a bright parade of young nurses and stewardesses—Penny Watson, Barbara Boyd, Shirley Turner—
who had never even heard of the places they were assigned
to and would never forget what they found there.

Robert Frost's haunting lines had special meaning for
Tom:

> *The woods are lovely, dark and deep,*
> *But I have promises to keep,*
> *And miles to go before I sleep.*

He went as far as he could go and died without knowing
whether the great journey he'd begun would ever be finished. But I have the feeling that he knows now, that he
rests easily in his eternal sleep, because men and women
of goodwill are on the move along the trail he blazed.

This is their story.

—MALCOLM W. DOOLEY

The Legacy of Tom Dooley

CHAPTER I

~~~~~~

Chaney

DR. TOM DOOLEY died of cancer on the evening of January 18, 1961, the day after his thirty-fourth birthday. It was a tragic end to an epic human story and the world took notice. His Eminence Francis Cardinal Spellman said that Dooley had achieved in his thirty-four years what few men manage in a scriptural lifetime. The high and mighty of many lands mourned him, and across Asia men and women who had never seen his face wept with the pain of personal loss.

In the ranks of MEDICO, the relief organization Dooley founded to bring a measure of respite to crushed and careworn multitudes, the volunteers were overcome and undone. Braced as they had been for Dooley's death, they were nonetheless hit so hard by the irrevocable fact of it that a continuing MEDICO appeared suddenly inconceivable. Who could take his place? Who else could provide the fiery inspiration, or attract the largess of drugs and dollars that was essential to their effort?

In each time and place there may be but one man who burns with a sense of mission, who finds impossible ways

1

to do impossible things, and so changes the way of the world. For MEDICO in Southeast Asia, Tom Dooley had been that man.

Others joined him. MEDICO, with no ties to government or any church, was organized to supply the Dooley field forces and channel the efforts of slowly growing numbers of Dooley volunteers. It stood for the Medical International Co-operation Organization and unlike other aid groups practiced therapeutic, not preventive medicine. "Very simply, what therapeutic medicine means," Dooley once said, "is passing out pills to people who are already sick."

By 1960, the medical missionaries of MEDICO had established seven hospitals in four Asian nations, and health projects in eight others. They pushed through jungles to remotest villages, sailed the dark rivers and marched across sun-scalded highlands to set up their bamboo clinics hard by the Red Chinese border, bringing aspirins, vitamins and penicillin—always with their own unmistakable sense of concern. And wherever they went, Dooley had already been, and regularly returned, sick now, but forever goading, leading, firing them to exceed themselves.

"Listen," he said, "I don't want you standing on some immaculate American pedestal reaching down to pull up the poor dirty Asian. You take off your nice white suit, understand? You get off the pedestal and you get down in the mud with them, knee-deep in the mud with them. Then you push."

"Kill this American spy!" cried Radio Peking and Radio Hanoi, but the people laughed. They revered Dooley. He was *Bac sy my*, Dr. America, and spoke to them in their own language, and became a legend in places where no other Caucasian had ever set foot. American critics taxed him with practicing nineteenth-century medicine and he cheerfully admitted it, further conceding that when he was gone the level might slip back another hundred years. "But don't you see," he chided them, "that this is some slight progress in a land where nearly everyone is living in the fifteenth century." There were reporters in Bangkok and Vientiane who called him arrogant and he didn't dispute them, either. "I know of but one meek and humble man who accomplished anything," he said, "and that was over nineteen hundred years ago." Then the wry Irish grin: "Anyway, I'm not so sure he was all that meek and humble."

And now, toward the end of a leaden winter day in New York, Tom Dooley slipped from coma to death. Melanoma, the black cancer that had been reaching outward from his chest for twenty-three harrowing months, finally tugged him into eternity. He had made a noble effort, written a shining bright chapter in the gray story of humankind. Now it was over.

And yet, was it? In some of the world's unlikely places that January day, a certain scattering of men and women, some of whom barely knew the name of Tom Dooley, heard the reports of his death and were particularly stirred, moved by a mysteriously felt intimation that though a man was dead his work was—or ought to be— imperishable and that they were somehow involved in it.

Margaret Alberding, a young Canadian nurse who had worked among the Indians and Eskimos of the north, heard the news in an Edmonton hospital, but for the moment was too busy with her duties to feel more than a fleeting sadness. Certainly she had no idea that her own life was to be forever and inalterably changed by this moment in time. But in the evening, she found her much-read copy of Dooley's first book, *Deliver Us From Evil*, an overwhelming account of how he had helped 600,000 North Vietnamese refugees flee to safety south of the demilitarized zone. She sat alone, bewildered that so serving and selfless a man need be cut off in mid-life. She assumed that MEDICO, too, was dead, yet for reasons she didn't clearly understand she found herself writing a letter to their New York address: did they have need of a nurse who was willing to go anywhere, do any kind of work, in the Far East?

Al Harris had gotten to know Dooley pretty well. One evening, on television, he had heard him tell of MEDICO's desperate need for money and capable volunteers. When the program ended, Harris turned off the set and went to the telephone. "Two hours and $30 later," he recalls, "I had tracked Dooley to Memorial Hospital in New York where he was undergoing a postoperative checkup. I said I wanted to go to work for him and he told me to come to New York. That summer I was in Quang Ngai."

Quang Ngai is a Vietnamese town on the South China Sea some 300 air miles north of Saigon. Here Harris worked in an improvised hospital in the charge of Dr. Carl Wiedermann—who had fled Nazi Germany at the age of fifteen—sometimes 20 hours a day, officially designated as laboratory and X-ray technician but in practice doing every job that needed to be done in the 100-bed ward, the clinic teeming each day with fresh casualties of the undeclared war. Dooley flew in often, the last time two weeks before Christmas, bringing small gifts for the staff. He brought Harris a leather key case and kept him up half the night talking medicine and supply problems. "He was on his way to the States for another checkup," Harris says, "and swore he'd be back in March. But he looked worn out and every move he made was agony, and you had the feeling that he was really here to settle things up."

Thirty-six days later, returning from Saigon with a load of supplies, Harris stepped off the train and was met by one of the Vietnamese hospital aides, near tears. "Dr. Dooley is dead," the man said in French, then could say no more.

Barbara Boyd had inward reasons to be moved by Dooley's death, though she had met him only a few times, and long before. The first time was alongside the swimming pool at the Princess Hotel in Bangkok in May, 1959. What was she doing in Bangkok, he asked. She explained that her father, a hydraulic engineer, had just finished a nine-month assignment in Ceylon and now he was taking the family back to the United States. Why did she want to go with them, he demanded, to waste her time and her youth, when there was plenty of work right here for a good strong girl. He would send her to his hospital in Muong Sing, where she was needed.

"I thought he was crazy," Barbara says. "I had just finished telling him that I'd spent what seemed like forever completely cut off from everything a nineteen-year-old kid cares about—baseball scores, dances, other nineteen-year-old kids—and he offers me *another* jungle to live in!"

In the most positive tone she could muster, she said that she was going home to get some glamorous job, as an airline stewardess, perhaps, and Tom Dooley could just keep his jungle. But Tom Dooley rarely let anyone off with the last word. "You'll change your mind," he said. "What you're looking for is right here, only you don't know it yet."

She forgot him and his wild idea as soon as the Boyds' flight took off for San Francisco, and within weeks she did, indeed, have a job as a stewardess. Then, a year later, she saw Dooley again. She was working a night flight out of St. Louis when he came aboard, limping, worn and wasted with cancer, yet only halfway through a nationwide lecture tour that was meant to raise $1 million for MEDICO. He was world-famous now, but feverishly conscious of the days overtaking him and all that needed yet to be done, grown out of patience with critics and questioners; and this led, 10,000 feet above the darkened Midwest, to a horrible little episode Barbara Boyd would never forget.

Dooley came forward to the lounge. He said again that he had meaningful work for her, that the people with the strength to do this work were *obliged* to do it. They owed something to those who were weak.

"What?" she asked moodily.

"A piece of themselves!" He grew angry. "Look, if you can teach one child from some Lao village to brush his teeth and wipe his behind you've done a big thing. Don't you see that? Don't you see that it's more important than jumping up every twenty minutes to get that old guy more Scotch?"

Across the aisle, the "old guy" heard plainly and looked up from his magazine. Appalled, Barbara fumbled for some saving way out and finally introduced Dooley as the well-known doctor who had dedicated himself to bringing medical care to Asia's farthest villages. Unappeased, the man harrumphed that, yes, he had heard of "the good doctor." Then he said, "I've also read that not all the people you're able to send out are fully qualified as physicians or nurses."

"I send people who will stay," Dooley came back. "That's the first requisite. If they're any good, they learn soon enough what they need to know."

"To practice nineteenth-century medicine?"

"For fifteenth-century diseases, right! Where do you live, may I ask?"

"Spokane, Washington."

"Yes, well when was the last time you had a case of malaria in Spokane, or bubonic plague? Typhoid, maybe? Yaws, cholera, amoebic dysentery? Those are fifteenth-century diseases, mister, and we get them all the time, every day. Treating them with nineteenth-century medical techniques is the best we can do and it beats the hell out of doing nothing at all!"

Barbara Boyd was never wholly satisfied with her "glamorous" airlines job after that. Based in Dallas, she took part-time work with some doctors, studied nursing, and Dooley's words—"Those who are strong enough to do it are *obliged* to do it!"—sprang often to her mind. In January she went east. She had been invited to President-elect Kennedy's Inaugural Ball and stopped in New York to visit her parents. There she heard that Dooley was back in Memorial Hospital and made up her mind to go see him, not at all sure of what she meant to say. But she caught cold and put the visit off for a day, then it snowed and she put it off for another. On the eighteenth, she felt worse and had to go to bed. And that night, on the 11 o'clock news, she heard the bulletin: Tom Dooley was dead.

There were others. Dr. Mary Davia remembered hearing Dooley tell a television audience how he won the goodwill of a witch doctor by giving him a chicken. "I guess that's fee-splitting," Dooley had said with a crooked smile, and Mary Davia thought, here is a man who is *doing* something. She was shaken by his death and wondered why other people seemed so untouched by it. Peter Purdy, then twenty-four and working for a press service in Denver, read that Dooley had died and was reminded somehow of a resolve he'd once made to help less lucky people find a better life. At Edwards Air Force Base in California, 2nd Lt. Juanita Tiffany, a nurse soon getting out of service, had been pondering what sort of work she might do. Now she thought she knew.

In Carmel, California, that day the first word was broadcast at 7 P.M., Pacific Standard Time. Two men listening in an otherwise silent house, expecting the grim news and dreading it, now finally began groping with the need to come to grips with it. One was the gloomy and reluctant heir of Tom Dooley's legacy, the man on whose shoulders the burden of holding MEDICO together—if, indeed, it could be held together—had just fallen. The other represented his best chance of success.

Dr. Peter Comanduras had been MEDICO's secretary-general from its inception in 1958. His base of operations was New York and he had left to Dooley the task of providing the driving force in the field. Inevitably, perhaps, this led to a divided outlook and the results were not always happy, never less so than in the last troubled months of Dooley's illness. Now Comanduras was in

California to address a MEDICO chapter, stopping in Carmel this pivotal night to see Dr. Verne Chaney who, not long before, had completed a special assignment for MEDICO in Cambodia, Laos and Vietnam. Chaney was fairly sure he knew why Comanduras had come—with Dooley dead, MEDICO needed a new Asian field director—and he searched his mind for an answer before Comanduras could pose the question. Chaney was a towering, thoughtful man of thirty-eight with an eminently successful practice in thoracic surgery. But it was not his commitment to private medicine that deterred Verne Chaney—although his friends would think him insane for abandoning a handsome income and a most comfortable way of life. Nor did he have any family ties to hold him. The real problem was Chaney's painful awareness of the split between MEDICO's field and office forces, and his doubt that from the fragments of conflict and the despair in the wake of Dooley's death he could patch together an effective effort.

Hours slipped by as the two men sat in the quiet house and summoned up memories of Dooley and of MEDICO's earlier, uncomplicated days. But the present with its inexorable demands was unavoidable. How to proceed? What to do? Comanduras said he thought the time had come to seek tangible help from Washington, that there was plenty of foreign aid money available if MEDICO was willing to operate under the umbrella of some government agency. "We're too big to be represented by amateurs in the field," he said earnestly, "no matter how noble their intentions. And we've got too much to do to forever be dependent on some nice lady's one-dollar contribution."

"But that's what it was supposed to be all about,"

Chaney replied. "People-to-people. No governments, no politics." He believed deeply in Dooley's essential conviction—individuals helping other individuals—and now he said, "Tom's whole idea was that we had to do it with our own two hands."

"Tom buried himself in those villages! He didn't know what our problems were. He didn't care."

Even as Dooley lay in death, echoes of the controversy sounded through the ranks. In November, Dooley had committed MEDICO to help equip the Avicina Hospital in Afghanistan, and had promised the Dalai Lama of Tibet two mobile health units for the thousands of refugees who had fled to northern India in 1959 when the Chinese marched into their benighted land.

Now Comanduras said to Verne Chaney: "We're in no position to provide those things, and Tom had no right to promise them. He wasn't even a member of the Board."

"But, Peter, in the name of heaven, he *was* MEDICO. He set up every program and installation we've got. He raised the money."

"I know what he's done and what we owe him. But we can't be a one-man show." Agitation drove him to his feet. He crossed the room, then spun back to say, "Anyway, Tom's dead now and MEDICO has to go on. I need somebody to take his place."

"No one can take his place," Chaney said darkly.

"Well, then, somebody to go out there and pick up the pieces the best he can. Will you do it, Verne?"

Chaney didn't answer. His most compelling instinct was to say Yes. He felt committed to MEDICO's work and had been restless ever since his return from Southeast Asia three months before. But there remained still the cleavage in viewpoints. If Dooley couldn't reconcile them, how could he? And if he didn't, how long would MEDICO endure?

It was near dawn when they finally tumbled into bed, nothing resolved, and the ghost of Tom Dooley still very much between them. Comanduras was to catch a 9 A.M. flight to Oakland for his lecture date, but overslept and Chaney volunteered to fly him up in his own small plane. And it was on the way north, the broad, blue Pacific off his left wing, that Chaney finally answered the question.

"What do you say, Verne?" Comanduras asked again. "Will you do it? For a year?"

And Chaney saw again those endless sick and their eyes that flickered with hope when the American doctor bent over them, and he said, "All right, Peter. For a year."

Verne Edward Chaney, Jr., never made a conscious decision that he would become a doctor. He simply always assumed it, through his high school days in Kansas City and undergraduate studies at Virginia Military Institute. He resigned an infantry commission during World War II to enlist as a private in the Army Medical Corps, then was discharged to attend the Johns Hopkins School of Medicine.

He was a restless type. During summer vacations he worked in remote mission hospitals along the Labrador coast. He likes to tell how he missed his first important diagnosis there—"which could have been very bad for my career because the patient was me." Not until his appendix had swelled to the size of an orange and burst did he realize that that persistent pain on his lower right side was more than simple indigestion, and by then it was too late for speedy evacuation. "They stuffed me with antibiotics and I knew if that didn't work they'd give me a decent burial. But they couldn't operate." Finally a plane slipped in to fetch him back to civilization and, following successful surgery, the fourth-year medical student—now especially skilled at spotting a troublesome appendix—returned to Johns Hopkins for his degree and a two-year residency in surgery.

The Korean War was a watershed in Verne Chaney's life. "I had a sort of guilt complex about having done so little in World War II and volunteered again as soon as I could." He calls the period when he served as a battalion surgeon in the 23rd Regiment the most significant of his life.

"There was a closeness and immediacy between doctor and men. You'd eat breakfast out of the same pot with a guy and two hours later they'd carry him in with his stomach laid open by shrapnel. To me this was what medicine was all about and I think I must have decided then and there that I had to be involved in the kind of work where people needed you right now."

Not even the battalion aid station was always close enough to where the action was to suit Chaney, with the result that he was himself shot up and returned home—a different man—with a Purple Heart, a Silver Star and the French Croix de Guerre. After three more years of general and thoracic surgical training, he accepted a post as chief of surgery at the Albert Schweitzer Hospital in Haiti. It proved to be fully the challenge he sought. The hospital, built by Dr. William L. Mellon, was in a primitive area that had never before had a medical facility of any kind, the people ridden by poverty and shackled by rites of voodoo. Chaney was to have stayed one year, was well into his second—and might have remained indefinitely—when he was unexpectedly caught up in the vortex of Caribbean politics.

A young American, held by the government of dictator François Duvalier, died under suspicious circumstances. Heart failure, announced Duvalier's flunkies. But Chaney, asked to do an autopsy by Ambassador Gerald Drew, saw on cursory examination that the man had been beaten to death, and he said so. There followed an angry dialogue between the Ambassador and the government, pressures, threats, and Chaney, who refused to alter his report, was forced to leave the country—and quickly.

He went to New York. Somewhere he had heard about Tom Dooley and his medical volunteers and felt that now he had something useful to offer to such work. Above all he wanted to get back overseas, to become involved, to be where the need was most immediate. But in the just-forming MEDICO office, he learned that both Dooley and Comanduras were in the Far East, and no one there seemed to think they were looking for a surgeon at the moment.

Chaney left his name. He started across the country, uncertain of what he would do or even where he was going. It seemed incredible to him that he could want so badly to serve in places where help was desperately needed, and that there was no way he could do this within a reasonable framework. He considered going back into the Army Medical Corps, but knew he would have to plow through five or six years of advanced military training before he could be of any real use. Westward bound, he inquired of other overseas agencies, but found them ecclesiastically oriented. "I think I'm a good Christian," he has said, "but I didn't want to carry a Bible to people whose beliefs are as valid as mine. I wanted to practice medicine."

He reached the west coast and visited his parents in Santa Barbara, then a Korean War comrade in Monterey. And as the plane circled the city, Verne Chaney gazed through his window and impulsively made up his mind that if he couldn't get overseas then he would live and work here on this lovely coast, and he didn't care if there was a chest surgeon on every other street.

As it turned out, there were none at all. Before long, Chaney had offices in Santa Cruz, San Luis Obispo, and Salinas, flying between them in his own airplane, taking on a partner to help with the mounting patient load, and watching his bank balance grow.

He kept in touch with MEDICO. Should they ever need a surgeon in the Far East—or anywhere—he wrote them, he was ready to go. In the spring of 1960, they were ready to send him. A magazine article had appeared faulting MEDICO and Dooley for practicing what the writer labeled "hit-and-run medicine." Typically, Dooley fired back:

"Don't judge Muong Sing by the standards of New York. We see 100 patients a day and can't afford the luxury of giving each one a two-hour workup. Besides, 80 per cent of these people have one or more of the same ten diseases, and those are the ones we're looking for."

But the article continued to trouble him. MEDICO was so totally dependent on the cash contributions of ordinary Americans that a widely read criticism of its work and effectiveness could undermine its ability to function at all. And if other reporters lit on other things to carp about . . .

Several urgent messages were exchanged between Muong Sing and MEDICO headquarters. Then Dr. Comanduras telephoned Verne Chaney from New York: was he still interested in going to work for them? If so, would he take on a three-month assignment to assist Dooley in a general program to improve MEDICO's surgical facilities—set up training procedures, purchase new equipment and do some special surgery himself? The call came in mid-May. By June 1, Chaney was on his way.

He went first to the MEDICO installation in Kratie, Cambodia, set up by Dr. Emmanuel Voulgaropoulos. Less than two years before, Voulgaropoulos had been interning at a Brooklyn hospital. Touched by the Dooley mystique, he promptly switched careers and led a medical team to the Far East. He and Chaney were to become fast friends.

In Quang Ngai, Chaney came to know Dr. Carl Wiedermann and Al Harris and in Muong Sing, Dooley aides Earl Rhine and Dwight Davis, two of MEDICO's earliest volunteers. But of course it was Doolcy himself who made the deepest and most lasting impression on Verne Chaney.

"It was impossible to believe that he had undergone a radical mastectomy half a year before," Chaney said. "He wore out ordinary men in a twelve-hour working day, then sat up half the night dictating answers to the hundreds of letters he got every week."

He never lost an opportunity to impress Chaney with the worth and direction of MEDICO's effort:

"We can go places government can't. Every connection these people have had with their government has been oppressive—tax collections, bureaucracy, war—and they instinctively transfer their suspicions to any other government. But we come in without guns and without speeches, just people, and when we take care of a sick kid it's pretty hard for its mother to be scared of us."

Yet he was fiercely proud of his country. Every

MEDICO installation flew the American flag and wherever he went he made it clear that his medicines were a gift of the American people.

He sought to impose no ideology or change anyone's religion: "Asians want help but they don't want to become American or communist to get it."

Medicine was the urgent need, but he knew that education was the ultimate salvation of these unenlightened millions: "I never give a pill without a little lecture on what it's for. Over the long haul what we leave behind in a man's mind is more important than what we leave in his digestive tract."

He had a coldly realistic view of his public relations worth: "Look, every time somebody snaps my picture it means maybe six more bottles of cough medicine on my shelf. Every time I get on a TV show, nickels and dimes and quarters come in for these hospitals. I'm just an instrument, a tool. I need people to buy my medicine and my plane ticket to Laos. I've got to be sold."

And with all that weighed on his mind, his illness and the burden of work, his sense of humor lit the long gray days and uplifted them all. To a visitor, obviously nervous about eating the native food: "Go ahead! I've been eating it for five years and all I've got is cancer."

His mission accomplished, Chaney returned to Monterey in September, 1960, and he saw Dooley for the last time that winter. They met in the St. Francis Hotel in San Francisco and Chaney was at once aware that Dooley had slipped badly. There was an ugly lump on his neck, obviously the metastasizing cancer, and he moved with pain-harassed weariness. But his personal fate troubled him only insofar as it affected MEDICO. He had underwritten its administrative costs with the royalties from his books and traveled 400,000 miles to raise nearly $2 million for operations. Now, with death only weeks away, he had to admit bleakly that his lifework was adrift, the MEDICO idea as he'd conceived and nourished it lost, like so many fine-sounding charities, in a front-office morass of vague and maudlin bureaucracy, no one to drive it back to the essential person-to-person theme, no one who believed, as he so desperately did, that one American volunteer in an Asian village was more meaningful to Asians than the most elaborate government aid program.

"He died convinced that MEDICO—*his* MEDICO— would die with him," Chaney has said, "and that was the real tragedy of his life."

Early in February, 1961, Chaney, now designated assistant to the secretary-general and executive field director for MEDICO's Asian Programs, flew off to the Far East. Despite the apparent difficulties, he went with a strong sense of optimism. Though the hospitals at Nam Tha and Muong Sing had had to be evacuated because of heightened Pathet Lao terrorism, there remained functioning MEDICO installations all over Southeast Asia.

But in Afghanistan he found that Comanduras's unwillingness to abide by Dooley's promise of staff and equipment for the new Avicina Hospital had produced predictable results: the Russians had promptly provided a complete surgery and the Afghans were bitterly disenchanted with their American "friends." In northern India, in the windswept mountains around Dharamsala, he was appalled by the spectacle of 40,000 Tibetan refugees, crowded into torn tents with no sanitation facilities, suffering from the diseases of malnutrition and enforced filth, hovering between life and death. They had fled the brutal Chinese invasion with little more than the clothing they wore and existed now at a bare level of subsistence. Those with enough strength yet to work hammered rock from dawn to dark to build up the sinuous, mile-high roads. Wages: 50 cents a day. Nowhere for hundreds of miles east or west was there a doctor or a nurse or medical aid of any kind.

Chaney requested an audience with the Dalai Lama, spiritual leader of Tibet, who himself had been forced to flee his homeland. He promised that Dooley's pledge of two mobile health units for the Tibetan refugees would be fulfilled. "I hadn't the faintest idea how, but I knew in my heart that it just had to be done."

Chaney moved on, still hopeful of pulling things together, but encountering new obstructions wherever he went. A program in Burma was bogged down in political antipathies. In Cambodia, Manny Voulgaropoulos had gone through one desperate period when his supply of essential drugs was totally exhausted. Now after two years in the field, he and his young wife were returning home— he was to become administrative field director—and though replacements were on the way, Chaney shuddered to think how newcomers would cope with the baffling silence that was New York's most frequent response to a plea for supplies. Everywhere, MEDICO people and programs suffered from poor communications and uncertain direction.

There was a single exception: Operation Vision. Under MEDICO sponsorship, an American ophthalmological surgeon of Washington, D.C., Dr. John King, had taken a medical team to Hong Kong and performed a series of corneal transplants. They also trained Oriental doctors in the transplant technique and established an eye bank program that over the years would restore the vision of thousands of men and women otherwise consigned to permanent blindness.

King had worked throughout much of India and Asia and he knew full well that the basic medical problems were too much dirt and not enough food. "In Korea," he reported, "the leading cause of blindness is smallpox— preventable by two cents' worth of vaccine." But the misconceptions, the grandiose visions, were hard to shake. More than once, on MEDICO surveys, King would be confronted by Asian doctors and pressed for fluoroscopes, cobalt machines and other highly sophisticated equipment. "It broke my heart. Every one of them wanted to establish another Mayo clinic when what they really needed for their people was plenty of soap and water and a good hot meal."

Meanwhile Chaney's troubles mounted. From New York he received a series of letters and cables from Voulgaropoulos, each one more discouraging than the last: Comanduras would not be persuaded to order the mobile health units; MEDICO's cash reserves were dropping at an alarming rate and the Tom Dooley Tribute Fund, set up for MEDICO's support under the patronage of President Kennedy and former President Eisenhower, was floundering so badly that of the $80,000 raised, more than $50,000 had already been dissipated in overhead. Finally, there came a wire from Voulgaropoulos warning that unless Chaney returned to New York at once and helped save the situation there would soon be nothing left to save. He left immediately.

But it was already too late. Chaney came back to an

endless round of wrangling and intensifying bitterness and there seemed no room for compromise. On July 9, in a last-ditch effort to salvage something from the dismal circumstances, Chaney and Voulgaropoulos went before the MEDICO board to tell their story and plead for some continuation of Tom Dooley's dream and purpose. The meeting lasted eight hours and ended with a resolution to accept the resignations of Drs. Chaney and Voulgaro-poulos.

"That was the worst time," Chaney recalls. But he could not bring himself to let go, to let the dream die, and he walked the summer streets, drank endless cups of coffee and brooded his way through the better part of a week. He *knew* what Dooley would have done—and one hot afternoon, walking alone on East Fifty-seventh Street, awed by the magnitude of his decision, he came to the conclusion that he had to do it himself. Late that after-noon, he telephoned Dooley's mother in St. Louis and told her that he wanted to set up a foundation in Tom's name, completely apart from MEDICO, to take over the programs Tom had begun and to carry on his work in Asia, and that he wanted her permission and support. And Agnes Dooley hesitated not at all. "You have them," she said.

How do you start a foundation? Verne Chaney hadn't the slightest idea, but he did know that Tom Dooley had had some firm friends in the New York business commu-nity, among them Samuel F. Pryor, vice-president of Pan American World Airways, and it was to Sam Pryor's office in the Chrysler Building that he brought his question: How do you start a foundation?

"Well, I don't know," came the cautious reply. "You need a board of directors, papers of incorporation. You need—say, what kind of foundation? What's this all about anyway?"

And so Chaney told him the whole story, the conflicts, the morass into which MEDICO had drifted and his own conviction that it was finished as the vibrant, person-to-person mission Dooley had envisioned.[1] "I want to establish a Thomas A. Dooley Foundation and start fresh. Will you be on the board of directors, Sam?"

The answer was yes and—still with nothing much more substantial than high hopes—Chaney was on his way. He enlisted others for his board and advisory council: Manny Voulgaropoulos, Carl Wiedermann, Tom Dooley's mother and his brother Malcolm, Admiral Arleigh Burke, and authors Eugene Burdick and William Lederer, who had first brought Tom Dooley's remarkable story to the *Reader's Digest* and so to the attention of the world.

One of Chaney's first decisions was to set up the new headquarters in San Francisco, as far from the old problems and the physical presence of MEDICO as possible. But he had one vital task left to do on the east coast. In August, he and Voulgaropoulos met in Oneonta, New York, home base of Medical Coaches, Inc., and asked to see the president, Ian M. Smith. Their conference was short and to the point. Chaney explained the Tibetans' appalling need for the two health units, then admitted that he could not promise to pay for them, and that at the moment he hadn't even enough money to get them to the west coast, let alone to Dharamsala, India.

"You are talking about $35,000," said Smith, "exclusive of transportation costs."

[1] MEDICO offices were closed in February, 1962; the organization then became a service of CARE.

"I see," said Chaney. "Well"—his own funds were exhausted: they might as well have been talking about $35 million—"I don't have it. I might be able to raise it . . ."

"Don't let that stop us," said Ian Smith, a man whose heart sometimes undid his balance sheets, and he promised to deliver the units in California before the end of the year. "We'll see about the money then."

Mrs. Dooley announced the establishment of the Thomas A. Dooley Foundation (TADF) at a press conference in San Francisco on September 15, 1961. It was an impressive, inspiring moment. No one mentioned that the bank balance of the just-born Foundation totaled $154, or that its headquarters was a telephone booth in the St. Francis Hotel. Nor were fund-raising prospects especially bright: just at this time the MEDICO-organized Tom Dooley Tribute Fund in St. Louis finally collapsed in bankruptcy. It was not unnatural for people reading this grim news to confuse the old Fund with the new Foundation. "Luckily we didn't have time to worry," Chaney said later, "or we'd have worried ourselves right out of existence."

The immediate problem—the continuing problem, the everlasting problem—was money. "When I first went with MEDICO they had $850,000 in the till," Chaney said recently. "I've been at this five years now and haven't raised that much." But somehow he has usually managed to scrounge, exhort and borrow enough to avert disaster.

He began by paying for the mobile health units. He had them delivered to Monterey where, under the direction of friends and supporters, they were moved from town to town and displayed in schools, shopping centers and vacant lots, and always with the same message: "Will you give a dollar to help us keep Tom Dooley's promise to the Tibetan refugees?" The dollars trickled in, and swelled to a flood when Carl Wiedermann, back to help launch TADF, suggested personalizing the gift by having each donor scratch his signature into the side of the van. Meanwhile a group of Dooley supporters in Chicago raised $5,000 to pay for a jeep and trailer, and Chaney covered the last $4,000 by taking out a personal loan. Finally, the thousands of signatures were shellacked over and the units shipped off to India.

Chaney kept pushing, driving himself to the limit of his endurance, and beyond. In Monterey he went from friend to stranger trying to raise money. In San Francisco he sought office space and furniture and volunteers. And four or five times each week he drove the 100-mile coastal road between them, always late at night, always fighting the sleep of total exhaustion and wondering whether there was any point to it, whether TADF would ever really get off the ground. By day and in the company of anyone who could help, he never expressed the shadow of a doubt. This was what Dooley would have wanted, he said with absolute certainty. It was necessary. It would work.

He found an office on Post Street—and the owner promised a $50-a-month contribution, the equivalent of a 25 per cent rent reduction. The Bank of America donated desks and chairs, IBM gave some typewriters, Kodak a Verifax copier and Olivetti an adding machine. The last was strictly for appearances—for months, there was no money at all to add or subtract. The staff, including Karen Rubio—a one-time MEDICO secretary who came to San Francisco at her own expense to help TADF get organized —was paid in fervent thank you's.

Chaney found himself in charge of everything—buying stationery and paper clips, arranging for printing and mailing lists and shipping and warehousing, none of which he had known anything about. And as always there remained the matter of raising money. "I hated that part of it worst," Chaney says. "Even when I was in private practice I had a hard time asking patients to pay their bills. And now here I was begging for a dollar, a filing cabinet, anything."

But he did it. He knocked on countless doors, waited in numberless anterooms, told his story over and over again, and when it fell on deaf ears he moved stubbornly on to the next prospect. He recalls it somberly:

" 'Great work,' they'd tell you. 'Keep it up.' But when it came to reaching for their checkbooks, so many of them would give you that, 'Well, maybe later. Maybe next year.' And these were people who had given generously to Tom. They responded to his personal challenge, his magic. But they couldn't relate to his work. They didn't understand that in a thousand Asian villages the people were *still* hungry and sick, and that it was *still* vitally important to us and to our country that we help."

Enough did respond, though, so that the TADF office could be set up on a permanent, if sometimes shaky, basis. Solid support was gained from substantial men and women of richly varied background: Henry Cabot Lodge, Spyros Skouras, California's then Governor Edmund G. Brown, Frank Sinatra, Dr. Edward Teller, General James Doolittle, Senator Jacob Javits, Bishop James Pike. Twelve TADF chapters were organized around the country. Singer Peggy Lee was elected chairman of the board and Eugene Burdick president.[2] When Albert Schweitzer was asked to be honorary chairman, he wrote: "I accept with all my heart. One of the most beauti-

[2] When author Burdick died in 1965, Actress Shirley MacLaine became chairman in 1967. Chaney became president, as well as executive director.

ful memories of my life is that of the day Dr. Dooley made a surprise visit to Lambarene. I am happy the Dooley Foundation has undertaken to continue his work. I am completely at your service."

Once the essential administrative details were provided for, Chaney was finally free to leave for Asia, where he most wanted to be and where the reestablishment of some medical programs was what all the organizational preliminaries were about. Of course he would never again be simply a doctor helping the people in some remote jungle—he bore *all* the TADF responsibilities now: administration, supply, personnel, as well as medical—but the closer he got to the work in the field the happier he was.

In December, 1961, he met Wiedermann in India and worked out the particulars of what came to be known as the stewardess program. It was an idea Chaney had had long before, encouraging U.S. airlines to grant stewardess-volunteers a two-or three-month leave of absence, on a rotating basis, and flying them to Asia where their special training would make them ideal TADF aides in hospitals and villages. Sam Pryor of Pan American became an enthusiastic supporter, as did other airline chiefs, and the program was launched that winter.

The mobile health units reached India in January and in the name of the Dooley Foundation, Chaney and Wiedermann presented them to the Dalai Lama and to the Indian government on the seventeenth, the anniversary of Tom Dooley's birth. In the months and years to come, they traveled thousands of precarious miles, circling landslides, inching their way along over the mountaintops to the separate camps—and bringing medical help to otherwise bereft thousands.

Chaney moved on to Laos. Government officials, bitterly disappointed that MEDICO had closed down all three of its hospitals, were hardly inclined to give *this* American an opportunity to disappoint them anew. But Chaney had traveled too far and given too much of himself to give up now. This new Foundation was in the Dooley spirit, he told Prince Boun Oum and Health Minister Touby Lyfoung. There would be no political or religious strings, and there would be a functioning hospital at Ban Houei Sai, the last place Tom Dooley worked— if they gave their permission. And again the magic of Dooley's name, the undying, incandescent glow he had cast and which his memory could still evoke in the Lao people, swung the balance. Approval was granted.

Carl Wiedermann, who only wanted to get back to the field, set out for the little mud-rut settlement of Ban Houei Sai on the banks of the Mekong. It was a risky assignment, not lightly undertaken. Pathet Lao terrorists, having overrun the hospitals at Nam Tha and Muong Sing, had now infiltrated far to the south and there was no assurance they would not soon control the area around Houei Sai. But as Wiedermann pointed out to Chaney, unless a TADF program was reestablished there, the whole of northern Laos would be without a doctor. And north he went, to paint and patch up the old hospital. Al Harris went with him.

Chaney went on to Vietnam. There, on a Saigon side street behind a high white wall, and on a small farm 12 miles away, a beautiful and iron-willed Tonkinese woman named Vu Thi Ngai cared for some 500 orphans, most of them the pathetic refuse of the wars that have torn Vietnam for 20 years. She had fled from Haiphong when the land was partitioned, bringing her charges with her. Tom Dooley had helped her reestablish the An Lac orphanage in Saigon and they had become fast friends. Now Chaney followed her on a tour of the neatly kept buildings, a swarm of active children at both their feet. He listened as she told how difficult it was for her to manage, since she felt obligated to take every child left on her doorstep; how she slept in a different place every night and rose at a different hour to take bread to the children at her farm. "The Viet Cong," she said in French-accented English, "do not like me because I have American friends."

"Are you afraid?" asked Chaney.

"To be afraid is natural. To hide in fear from what one must do is not to live at all."

Before he left, Chaney promised her all the help in drugs, money and clothing that TADF could manage. The last of the Foundation's four fledgling programs had been launched.

In the seven years since those early uncertain days, Verne Chaney has known disappointment and great gratification. He would like still to be performing surgery in some small Asian hospital, but there are too many other things to be done and he alone can do them. "We need a man to run the office and another to make the speeches and another to raise the money and another to run the overseas operations. Unfortunately, we can't afford to hire one of those men, let alone all four." *Somehow,* though, he does it alone.

There have never been more than two people on the office payroll—though volunteers often work until 10 P.M. —and the annual budget only last year topped $100,000. Chaney recently pointed out that it costs $10,000 a day to operate the hospital ship *Hope*. "It's a fine, noble effort, no question, but for $10,000 I could run Ban Houei Sai for a year."

There has never been enough money, and it has sometimes been in perilously short supply. "The truth is that the Dooley Foundation ought to have gone down the drain years ago," Chaney said recently, and wryly added, "but I kept telling them I didn't know how to fill out the bankruptcy forms. So here we are, still in business."

It grieves him that the Foundation is sometimes hard to sell. "It is so important to the well-being of other people, *and* the well-being of Americans. The Foundation doesn't consist of do-gooders. We're selfish. We serve ourselves serving others. And the people we want must be selfish. If they don't get something out of this, they're wasting our time. They must believe in the interdependence of all people. They must understand that every patient they treat becomes a friend of America."

Health in the developing nations, he says, has little to do with aspirins or penicillin. It is a matter of economics and education and the standard of living. "But penicillin buys us time while the standard of living catches up. That's why it's vital for us to be there, to pass out the aspirins and stand by for emergencies. It's like surgery: the first thing you have to do is get the patient off the table."

CHAPTER II

On the Other Side of Greenwich Village

AL HARRIS HAD a fearful stutter. It plagued his youth and shaped his later years. Grown to lanky young manhood, his face was dark and usually pinched in thought, plainly revealing the intensity with which he felt things. Brooding dark eyes looked out on a world that bruised him easily and often and against which his best defense was withdrawal.

His father had died when he was six and he was raised by grandparents in Maryland. But even after his mother remarried and bought two old brownstones on East Tenth Street in New York's Greenwich Village, Al spent holidays and long weekends with her and was close to her and to his stepfather. He came to feel, too, special affection for the mixed bag of humanity that rented the furnished rooms in the brownstones—alcoholics, illiterates, the lovelorn and lost who depended on his mother, not only for bed and board, but to help them cope with a world that made no allowance for their frailties. She nursed them when they were sick and sobered them up when they got drunk. She found them jobs, wrote their letters and listened to their woes. They were children, she once told Al, and somebody had to be their mother.

This matter-of-fact sense of compassion became part of Al Harris's nature, too. As a medical technician in the navy, he passed most of his off-duty hours prowling around the sick bay, delivering mail and cigarettes, filling in as a fourth in a bridge game, sharing scuttlebutt with men whose only reality was a three-by-six hospital cot.

He left the service after four years of duty in Europe and the Caribbean and came back to Maryland, now twenty-four years old, to enroll in Hagerstown Junior College, and to take full-time work in a medical laboratory and a night job with a funeral home: after 8 P.M. he was responsible for all calls, picking up the cadaver and assisting in the embalming process. For each call he received $20. By the time he happened to see Tom Dooley on television that May evening in 1960, he was worn out, dissatisfied with the dreariness of everything he was doing and absolutely primed for some more meaningful challenge.

On Monday he cut his classes and took the bus to New York to keep his appointment with Dooley, worrying all the way that he'd be found unqualified or stutter himself into rejection. But Dooley, just a few days out of the hospital and temporarily settled in the MEDICO office on Lexington Avenue, seemed unconcerned with the *person* of Al Harris. There were a few questions about his background, then he asked why Al wanted to go to work for MEDICO.

And certain he was scuttling his last chance, Al heard himself rattling out the truth: "B-because I'm s-sick of working myself into a lather and getting nothing out of it but some money. I want to do something for m-me."

The interview was all but over. Dooley, who had a

pathological suspicion of applicants proclaiming a yen to sacrifice themselves in the cause of "poor, suffering Asians," was well satisfied with Al Harris's credentials. "You'll be assigned to Vietnam," he told him abruptly. "Come back here in a month and we'll send you out with a team."

By the end of June, he was back in New York, packed, vaccinated and ready to ship out. But as he was to find out time after exasperating time, MEDICO rarely moved in such a straightforward direction. A new hospital was to be established at Quang Ngai on the Vietnamese coast; until the rest of its American staff was assembled, Al would work in the New York office sorting and shipping medical supplies. Typically, Dooley used the time to raise money, lecturing on MEDICO's work and purpose anywhere he could find an audience. Whenever he spoke in the New York area, Al Harris tagged along. "Listen to what I say," Dooley once told him drily. "It's about the only training you'll get."

On July 18 the Quang Ngai team was finally outward bound—Al and two other young corpsmen, Reggie Gordon and Bill Gagion, and a gaunt, Lincolnesque doctor of thirty-two named Carl Wiedermann, who had survived the chaos of Hitler's Germany and now bore on his soul a small scar for each human agony to which he had ever been witness. Dooley, of course, led the way, and there were stops in Honolulu, Hong Kong and Saigon. And the closer they came to their destination, Al recalls, the more open and intense grew the devotion of the people to their *Bac sy my*. "He had spoken of Asia as his home, and finally I understood why."

In Hong Kong they shopped for medical supplies and personal equipment. Dooley knew exactly where to get the best prices, and he knew how to bargain his way below those. The team members scurried along in his wake, exhausted by the heat, bewildered by the frenzy of the Hong Kong shops and streets. But Dooley drove on, and one particularly arduous afternoon, Bill Gagion faintly noted that, "If Dooley is supposed to be dying I would hate like hell to follow him around when he's well."

The next stop was Saigon where they passed the first days fighting off the debilitating effects of the relentless dysentery that seems to overtake all Westerners on their first visit to the Orient. "Ho Chi Minh's Revenge," they called it, not laughing. When they could muster the strength, they went on shopping for essentials, all of which—including a Vespa motorbike—had to be stored in their room at the Majestic Hotel. "It looked like the stockroom at Macy's," said Al, "and just climbing over it on your way to bed was enough to ensure a good night's sleep."

Before he left, Dooley had taken them to Madame Ngai's An Lac orphanage and soon they were regular morning visitors there, pitching in to help care for the hundreds of children to whom this high-walled enclosure was home, and the soft-eyed woman in the immaculate white dress mother, father and guardian angel. Once Vu Thi Ngai had lived in the North Vietnamese town of Thanh Hoa near the Gulf of Tonkin. Her family was the wealthiest in the canton and her husband was a good man, and they had a great lovely house surrounded by rich fields and two fine children and life was full. Then, in a few cataclysmic weeks in 1946, everything changed. The Viet Minh came and there were bloody battles. Vu Thi Ngai's husband was killed and her house destroyed and, suddenly, everywhere there were abandoned children wandering the streets and scrounging in garbage cans for a morsel of nourishment, and orphaned babies with no one even to hear their despairing last cries.

At first Madame Ngai brought them to her ruin of a house and fed them as best she could. But the Viet Minh drive was inexorable and soon she had to flee. She took her jewels and some gold and her little brood of cast-out humanity and slipped away, running now south, now north, stopping wherever it seemed safe, to buy and beg shelter and food and clothing for her charges. Five times in six years she was driven from provisional havens, her money melting away and her burden of tiny refugees growing until, by the time she reached Haiphong in 1952, more than 600 children of all ages depended on her for life itself.

In Haiphong she established the An Lac orphanage— three small abandoned buildings and a few sprawling sheds with tin roofs and ragged canvas sides which did little to ward off slashing monsoon rains. And here Tom Dooley found her in August, 1954, when he arrived with the American mission charged with assisting in the epic "Passage to Freedom," the temporary care and ultimate evacuation of 600,000 refugees from the communist-conquered north.

Between the needful, dark-eyed orphans and the free-wheeling naval doctor there sprang up a kind of instant love affair. Dooley regularly took them in groups of 30 or 40 to the American ships in Haiphong Harbor, where bemused crewmen fed them ice cream and showed them movies. He wrote to the Mead-Johnson Company in Indiana and unabashedly asked if they would send him vitamin "samples" to provide daily doses for 600 children for six months. They sent enough to last 1,000 children a year. For her part, Madame Ngai revered the *Bac sy my* and invariably kept a bottle of good sound bourbon on hand for his visits, and how she ever came by such a treasure was only further evidence of her remarkable ingenuity. In May, 1955, when the time came to move the orphanage to South Vietnam—beds, bassinets, rice bowls, children and all—Dooley had a hand in finding them permanent quarters in Saigon, sent his aide, Norman Baker, to make certain that the transfer went smoothly, and assured Madame Ngai—though the words were hardly necessary —that he would help her however he could.

And so the An Lac orphanage eventually came under the protective wing of MEDICO. And Madame Ngai, her own two children grown and gone to France, continued to care for waifs and strays wherever she found them and somehow managed a measure of love for each. Dooley once wrote that though she was probably past sixty, she looked like a woman of thirty at her loveliest and had the spirit of a girl of sixteen. Six years later, when Al Harris and the other new MEDICO volunteers first came to An Lac, she hadn't changed, and they were captivated by her. And they found, as had Dooley, that when their spirits were unusually low, the laughter at An Lac, where no one had much to laugh about, was a tonic and restorative.

One mid-September morning, Al Harris and Bill Gagion dragged most of their mountain of supplies aboard the northbound coastal train and set off at last for Quang Ngai. Dooley had flown south to Malaya where he hoped to set up another MEDICO hospital. Dr. Wiedermann and Reggie Gordon remained in Saigon one week more to unsnarl the last of the red tape.

The train was known as the Suicide Express. Although Quang Ngai was little more than 300 miles from Saigon, it averaged 22 hours getting there, and sometimes didn't get there at all. For the Viet Cong had a disconcerting habit of blowing up the tracks, or of simply halting the train for a tense hour or two just to demonstrate their mastery of the countryside. Limping into the hospital compound in the ominous hours before dawn, the young volunteers, raspy-eyed and bone-weary, had finally begun to understand the nature of the land where they had come to work.

In all the eight years of war between the French colonials and the Viet Minh, the province of Quang Ngai had been a communist stronghold. Its capital, also known as Quang Ngai, was pressed to the sea by deep green mountains, a nervous little city of 3,000 inhabitants on the eastern flank of the narrowing neck of land that runs 200 miles to the North Vietnamese border. In happier days it had been a fashionable seaside resort and so boasted electricity and even some running water. A beginning had been made on a provincial hospital, but constant Viet Minh raids had long ago caused it to be abandoned. Now the streets that had been so proudly paved were cracked and weed-grown, and the people in their grass huts with the thatched roofs lived in poverty and fear.

The 1954 Geneva Accord, which finally ended France's Indochinese adventure, required the Viet Minh to withdraw to the north behind a demilitarized zone partitioning the two Vietnams. But no sooner had they gone than their communist compatriots in the South, the Viet Cong, infiltrated the province and began a ceaseless struggle to retake it and its strategically situated seat of government. And in the remorseless guerrilla campaign that followed

—villages put to the torch, pillage and kidnappings—there were two civilian casualties for every soldier hurt, and these luckless wounded wandered the countryside seeking help and there wasn't any. For in all Quang Ngai province with its 700,000 souls, there was only a French-trained male nurse, lavishly called *médecin chef*—head doctor—but whose medical skills beyond basic first aid were illusory.

Dooley's original idea had been to build the first MEDICO hospital in Vietnam at the 17th parallel, hard by the DMZ. He had a penchant for pushing as close to Red frontiers as he could get, for he believed that in these places the people's needs were most acute. But South Vietnamese President Ngo Dinh Diem urged him to go to Quang Ngai. "There is no worse place in the country," he said, "but no place needs your medicines more."

Now, as the hot September sun rose over the compound, Al Harris and Bill Gagion had their first close look at the hastily completed hospital. There was a main building of mud and straw, large enough for twenty bed patients—although there were only ten beds—and three smaller "hard" buildings: one of these was to be used for surgery and X rays, another for the daily clinics and laboratory work, with the third serving as the staff's living quarters. Already in residence was the *médecin chef*, whose name was Sau Baa and who eyed the newcomers warily and replied to their questions in politely evasive monosyllabic French.

Al and Bill were not put off. Dooley had carefully explained to the new MEDICO team that in the very nature of things they represented a threat to the *médecin chef*. "You've got to show him—explaining is no good—

that you are not here to rob him of his dignity, that you will not cause him to lose face with the local people. Remember, up till now he's been the only medicine there was in these parts. Here we come with our high-powered ideas and our fancy equipment and you can't expect him to like it. But you *can* let him do everything he has the ability to do, then help him learn to do more. Because he'll be here long after we're gone, and others like him, maybe better trained, and in the long run the health of all these people will depend on them, not us." So the young Americans deferred to Dr. Baa and the three plunged into the work of readying the hospital for the first caseload of patients.

Nothing could have prepared them for their numbers. On the first morning after the arrival of Dr. Wiedermann and Reggie Gordon, a bleak line of men, women and children wound away from the outpatient clinic to a muddy field 150 yards in the distance. Roosters harangued at the thin, early sun Pigs and mangy dogs, brought along by the Vietnamese who had no place to leave them, milled in hapless circles and snorted and bayed. Only the people stood quietly, patiently, even when all at once it began to rain and in seconds they were drenched. Surveying the overwhelming scene from the steps of the staff house, Bill Gagion said, "I've got to take a picture of this."

And Carl Wiedermann said, "You haven't got time. We have work to do."

And so they began.

As news that the American doctors had come to Quang Ngai flitted from village to village, the incredible lines lengthened day by day. What the MEDICO team now referred to as sick call began averaging 300 patients a session with peaks of nearly twice that many. "Look at this pathology," Wiedermann muttered in gloomy awe one morning as they walked past the ragged file to the clinic. "Do you know, I could choose any one of a dozen diseases —dysentery, typhoid, tetanus, leprosy, malaria, TB—and pull enough cases out of that line to keep all of us busy, treating nothing else, all day long."

They could never afford that luxury. Their hours, beginning at 5:30 A.M., fell into rigid, exhausting routine. By 7 they were checking their hospital patients: the wounded, the victims of tuberculosis, malnutrition and parasitic infestation, most of whom lay on mats on the floor. The beds were reserved for those with at least two of these afflictions in combination. Then, and for as long as it took to go through that silent, stoic line, the clinic was open. Before long they had worked out a system that gave them at least an even chance to be finished by lunchtime: Dr. Baa saw each patient first, bandaging cuts and bruises and dispensing medicine for the simple ailments he recognized; all the rest he passed through to the MEDICO corpsmen, who in turn screened out all the patients they could cope with, sending the difficult cases—the severely wounded, suspected tuberculars, malignancies, beriberi, leprosy—on to Carl Wiedermann.

Lunch called for an earnest effort of will for nearly a year, since their Vietnamese cook, though cheerful and willing, was a slow learner and found it hard to understand what was wrong with unplucked chicken heads floating in the soup, or how anyone could not be fond of fish eyes. Glad to leave the table, the volunteers made hospital rounds again, did laboratory tests and, in whatever hours of daylight remained, worked away at construction of several new buildings—an isolation ward for tuberculosis cases, a screened-in kitchen to replace the open campfires that attracted a Noah's Ark of hungry animals, and a four-compartment toilet to discourage the patients from using the nearby canefields—the original toilet had long since plunged into its own hole.

At any given time, the population on hospital grounds, sick and well, was three or four times the number of bed patients. This was because it was the practice for entire families to make the journey to Quang Ngai with their ailing member, and if the diagnosis called for hospitalization they all stayed, pigs, chickens and dogs, as well. Wiedermann and his assistants were particularly moved by the mute pleas in the eyes of parents whose children lay ill with the whole host of infectious diseases—pneumonia, meningitis, tetanus, empyema—that preys on the undernourished and unwashed. Yet despite liberal use of antibiotics, to which such diseases should promptly respond, the twenty-odd children on the medical ward grew weaker and sicker and many were plainly close to death.

Late one night, as the Americans sat around their table, baffled, beset by their anxiety, Dr. Baa at a respectful distance in the shadow, Wiedermann began to question his diagnoses. He felt all things deeply and his emotional reserves had been heavily drawn on long ago and now, torn as though each sick child was his own, he lashed out at himself: "They ought to get better! I must be wrong."

"On all of th-them?" Al asked.

"Well, why don't *any* of them get better? You take a kid who's supposed to have simple pneumonia. You give him streptomycin and plenty of good nourishing food and, damn it, he's supposed to respond!"

"No eat food," Dr. Baa said quietly in his new English.

They turned slowly into the shadows. The dark little man with the shiny hair wet his lips. "Here, when small ones sick, mother give no more food," he said, "only maybe little rice soup. Vietnamese village people think sickness get hungry, leave body."

"But I've taken trays down for those kids myself," Reggie Gordon said.

"Father eats, and mother, sisters, brothers. Don't want waste. Don't want hurt Tom Dooley men."

Baa looked embarrassed. The others sat slack-jawed with astonishment as the truth finally gained a foothold in their minds: the patients on the children's ward were starving to death.

"How could they do that?" Gagion said under his breath. "They'll kill them, their own kids."

"They don't know," Wiedermann said. He looked away. "God, when I think how much *we* don't know, and we're civilized!"

He could hardly contain himself. With first light he was down on the children's ward, surrounded by warm milk and boiled eggs, prompting in English as Baa explained to the startled Vietnamese that the little ones had to be fed or they would die. Thereafter, for a full week, he appeared at the ward each mealtime, nodding encouragement as wary mothers spooned food into eager mouths. Then, abruptly, the battle was won: eyes brightened with returning health, cheeks showed color and wasted bodies filled out. One by one the young patients went home and the Quang Ngai Dooley team had scored a first victory over its most implacable foe, ignorance.

Day in, day out, and in countless ominous ways, the Viet Cong made their presence felt. Not a week passed without a dozen or more battle casualties, military and civilian, and on some nights when the fighting flared close by, as many as sixty wounded straggled and limped and were carried to the hospital. Then the asthmatic old generator wheezed on until daybreak and under the glaring operating-room light Carl Wiedermann, with Al and sometimes Reggie assisting, sliced away torn flesh and excised metal and dirt and stitched up the mutilated bodies as best as he could. And whenever there was a momentary lull, Wiedermann slipped outside and quietly vomited.

They treated members of the Viet Cong, too, at first only those who were brought in more dead than alive and writhing in terror at the exquisite tortures with which the American devils awaited them. But when there was no torture, only the same care given to everyone else on the ward—except that the Vietnamese nurses shunned them— the V.C. soldiers perked up and confided to anyone who would listen that they were only simple villagers forced at gunpoint to fight against the government. Their lame explanations didn't matter. Wiedermann said everything that needed saying the first time he had to decide whether or not he was going to care for the enemy: "That man needs a doctor and I'm a doctor. Take him inside."

And perhaps because the Dooley hospital practiced impartial, nonpolitical medicine, the Viet Cong never attacked it, nor did they molest any of the corpsmen when they drove the Vespa or the rattling jeep on calls to outlying villages. Al Harris says there were times when he could *feel* himself framed in a gunsight, but no shot was ever fired at him and only rarely did he even see a Viet Cong. And as time passed and the esteem in which the Americans were held grew and spread through the province, they felt even more secure, for the V.C. effort to win

over the villagers would have been seriously undermined
if it were known that they'd harmed any of the MEDICO
people.

Then some new tactical consideration started Viet
Cong units mining the roads at night. This *was* a cause for
concern: no matter what the intent, a land mine doesn't
distinguish between friend and foe. But the only casualty
they knew of in the immediate vicinity was a South Vietnamese army truck, the front end of which was blown into
the four corners of a roadside rice paddy one afternoon.
Returning from an overnight visit to a distant village, Al
and Dr. Baa got out to see what could be done about moving the derelict to one side so their jeep could get by.
There followed an impassioned exhortation by the army
driver which swept right through Baa's feeble attempts at
interruption. Finally the soldier paused for breath and Al
asked, "What's he s-saying? What's the matter?"

Baa turned on him a face full of stunned confusion. "He
say we drive over road yesterday—we should have tell him
V.C. put mine in it."

As Baa's confidence in himself and his American colleagues grew, his medical skills broadened and he became a genuinely effective doctor. In the presence of
Vietnamese patients, Wiedermann never failed to ask for
his ideas or opinions on a diagnosis and at his suggestion
Baa undertook to train local nurses to man dispensaries
in the larger villages. These he regularly supplied and
checked on himself. With pride and great effort the
médecin chef had slowly grown into the important num-
ber-two role at the hospital.

"Carl Wiedermann kept the whole operation stuck together," Al recalls. "He was the one who made a doctor
out of Baa. And he made believers out of the local offi-

cials. They became our friends and they bailed us out of trouble more than once."

It was the Governor of the province who made possible the establishment of an urgently needed blood bank. The first blood transfusion ever given in Quang Ngai was performed by Wiedermann with a small hand pump, a direct transfusion unit, only a few days after the Dooley team's arrival. Into the hospital that morning came one of the town's seven policemen, flat on his back on a makeshift litter carried by anxious relatives, deadly pale and barely conscious. A cursory examination was all that was required to diagnose a hemorrhaging gastric ulcer, a massive loss of blood and a dismal prognosis.

"All right, you men," Wiedermann said to everyone in earshot, "roll up your sleeves and let's see who comes closest to matching this guy's blood."

Reggie Gordon won the dubious honor. He stretched out tensely on the next bed, clenching and unclenching his fist to help the little pump transfer blood from his vein to the vascular system of the wasted Vietnamese. And the therapy worked. Before long the patient's eyes focused and gazed back with interest at the worried faces above him, and when the worst of the internal bleeding was under control he was carried to the operating room. Two weeks later he was discharged and went home proclaiming himself half-American because he had been honored by *Bac sy* Gordon's blood, and extolling the magic curative power of the transfusion.

But his audience was limited and suspicious—to give blood, the Vietnamese believed, was to drain away the essence of life—and for a long time the Dooley staff members were Quang Ngai's only donors. They talked themselves hoarse but convinced no one else to give blood.

They bled themselves weak, then watched helplessly as wounded soldiers and children undergoing simple surgery died for want of a pint of blood. One night they lost a little girl who hemorrhaged during an appendectomy and Carl Wiedermann came out of the surgery red-eyed and wretched with anger. "We've got to have a supply of blood!" he said. "We've got to have a blood bank!"

"How?" Al asked bleakly. "It's easier to get a p-pint of sperm from these people than a p-pint of blood."

"I'll find a way," Wiedermann promised.

Later that week the Governor of the province came to inspect the hospital and was duly impressed, and Wiedermann had his idea. "Will you stay for lunch, Governor?" he said politely. "There's a matter I'd like to talk over with you."

He talked long and he talked hard. First he persuaded the Governor of the life-and-death need for a blood bank. Then, fighting the man's personal fear, centuries-old superstition and the ever-crucial matter of face, he convinced him that he—and only he!—could help them establish one. And he told him how.

Early the next day, the MEDICO men drove to the center of town, their jeep hauling a trailer full of lumber. By 11 A.M. they had constructed a low platform in the square, attracting a fair crowd of curious onlookers, which swelled and buzzed and pressed close when the corpsmen produced a bed and set it down in the center of the platform.

Promptly at noon the Governor and his entourage appeared. By this time the square was packed tight with people, all straining for a look, all passing back to less favored spectators behind them fanciful versions of what was happening. Tapping his swagger stick uneasily against his thigh, the Governor mounted the platform. Now everyone could see, and when he rolled up his sleeve and lay down on the bed in his impeccable uniform and polished boots a puff of astonishment scurried around the square.

"The Governor is ill!"

"But why do they put him to bed in the street?"

"Who knows? The Americans have strange ways."

Al Harris knelt by the side of the bed. He tried to smile reassuringly, but the Governor's eyes were tightly closed, as were his lips and his fists. But only Harris could see how frightened he was and Al Harris kept smiling. He tied a rubber tube around the Governor's upper arm until a rick dark vein appeared. Deftly he slid the sterile needle into it, then firmly opened and closed the Governor's fingers until vivid red blood flowed into the bottle held aloft by Bill Gagion so everyone could see it. Now the crowd's gasp was sharp and vehement, and Carl Wiedermann, standing nervously with Reggie at the foot of the platform, whispered, "Be sure he drinks all that bouillon before he tries to get off the bed. If he passes out on us we have a very good chance of getting lynched."

But the Governor didn't pass out. In ten minutes the entire procedure was over and he rose, grinning with relief, and rolled down his sleeve. He shook hands with each of the Dooley men and walked calmly to his car, the crowd falling back to open a path as though he had come directly from an audience with Buddha. Nor did the Americans say a word. With a last flourish of the full red bottle, they climbed into the jeep and returned to the hospital, leaving a crew to dismantle the improvised hematology lab.

No words were needed. The Governor's brave example—and the obvious fact that he hadn't died—persuaded enough other hardy souls to yield to Wiedermann's entreaties and a modest blood bank was finally begun. It grew and was replenished by civil servants, soldiers, office-seekers, all of whom the Governor periodically and pointedly reminded that if *he* could give blood . . . Long after Wiedermann and Al Harris moved on and were replaced by other Dooley volunteers, the Quang Ngai blood bank flourished and remained one of the hospital's significant assets.

Although the spectrum of disease in each village was broad beyond belief, tuberculosis was the great killer. Wiedermann once calculated that on the basis of his comprehensive sampling of patients, one out of every seven people in the province was afflicted, which made 100,000 tuberculars in Quang Ngai alone. And there were 32 provinces in South Vietnam. Without treatment, the deadly course of the disease was inexorable and the rate of contagion rampant.

The Dooley team tackled the problem head-on. Within weeks of their arrival the screened-in, 30-bed TB ward was completed and the everlasting job of diagnosis and treatment begun. At first, having no proper X ray, they worked with an old French fluoroscope and an even older microscope. But with these two pieces of equipment the lethal lung shadow and elusive tubercle bacillus could be detected. Hour after endless hour Al stood in the dark at Wiedermann's shoulder learning to recognize TB lesions while patients coughed at them through the fetid air of the narrow little X-ray room. In six months he was reading fluoroscopies alone. "I had no real business doing that," he has said, "but the man was staggering with exhaustion."

The man, Wiedermann of course, checked each diagnosis with sputum specimens. The most acute cases were put to bed in the isolation ward—when there was room. All the rest, among them some very sick people indeed, were given isoniazid, an anti-tuberculosis specific, vitamins and four vials of streptomycin, and sent home with instructions to return in two weeks.

"That's not the way you treat TB in New York," Al says wryly, "but we were a long way from New York and there wasn't much else we could do. Anyway, it worked."

It worked because they drove their weary bodies and racked their brains to make it work. When a patient didn't come back for his semi-weekly examination and more medicine, they went looking for him—and while they were in the village lectured on the danger of permitting children to sleep with tubercular parents. To accommodate the strong Vietnamese sense of pride—and underline the importance of medication—Wiedermann imposed a small fee for the streptomycin vials, and accepted a chicken, some eggs or a pound of potatoes from those who hadn't the necessary few piastres. Failing even that, he sent totally insolvent patients out to cut weeds for an hour, then their indebtedness was paid.

The entire TB program, like the MEDICO hospital itself, was only a bare beginning in the great sea of disease. But to the thousand or more souls who didn't die in choking travail before their time it was the most important thing that ever happened. And to millions of other Vietnamese, whether they knew it or not, it was a first faint stirring of a future hope.

To everyone they reached, the Dooley men brought a timid new optimism that went beyond sickness and health. For uncounted generations the impoverished Asian masses had gulped their religion fatalistically, and it had narcoticized them. Whenever things went badly, when a child died and the harvest was poor and taxes high, it was invariably ascribed to the will of God. They hadn't the strength to think their way beyond this simplistic and hopeless dictum. Now, seeing all at once that the dying didn't have to die, that the crippled might walk again and the sick get well, they began to believe that all their tomorrows didn't have to be like all their yesterdays, that the son didn't have to resign himself to the father's poverty—that there was something new under the sun.

The months passed, the hot spring and the hotter summer, then the swollen monsoons loosing cascades of rain. Only the work and the everlasting forays of the Viet Cong were unchanging. One October night they attacked a village five miles from the hospital during the height of a harvest feast, shooting and bayoneting and burning the straw houses at will. Out from Quang Ngai went the government troops with their 1912 rifles, and plain citizens armed with spears and sticks and in bare feet, and they drove the marauders off. But all that night and into the next day the wounded made their way to the hospital and when it was all done there were nine dead. Among them was a seven-year-old boy with a bullet hole in his chest. Not all of Carl Wiedermann's defiant efforts could save him, and in the afternoon his family brought some warped lumber and made a coffin to carry him home in.

After that it rained for a month. At night the hospital staff would sit in weary stupor listening to the radio wane and shrill until it was time to go to sleep. And it was on such a night, in the midst of a stuttering Vietnamese harangue from Radio Hanoi, that they heard their own names spoken and repeated.

"W-what the hell was that all about?" Al asked Dr. Baa. "He say you come poison people with American medicine. He tell people—drive Americans out." Baa laughed at the foolishness of it but the sound came out hollow. They all knew that this was only a beginning.

When they set out for the clinic next morning, they found that the Governor had provided an armed guard for their protection, two soldiers who went where they did, even to the door of the toilet. But no Vietnamese came "to drive the Americans out"—they came, as always, only to have their hurts and illnesses cared for—nor did the Viet Cong disturb them any more than before. But having learned the nature of the antagonist, they waited for the other shoe to fall.

It did, with a resounding echo, ten days later. In a raid on a Catholic hospital not far from Saigon, the V.C. hauled all the medical supplies to the center of the town for a ceremonial burning. But before putting the torch to desperately needed drugs, bandages and equipment, all donated by American agencies, public and private, they plucked some medicines from the pile and triumphantly showed the terrified townspeople that the effective date stamped on the bottles had come and gone. "Poison!" they cried, firing the priceless lot. "That is all the American devils have for Vietnamese people, poison!"

It was a vivid story and the V.C. made sure it reached the farthest hamlet. And there must have been many places where its propaganda effect was considerable, since the average Vietnamese could hardly be expected to know that outdated penicillin or streptomycin, while losing a little of its potency, remains effective and holds absolutely no hazard by reason of its age. At the Dooley hospital, the problem was not the patients—who knew well enough the value of the medicine they had been given—but the Minister of Health. Two days after the raid he ordered Wiedermann to get rid of all his outdated drugs so that if the Viet Cong struck Quang Ngai they would be denied another propaganda windfall.

The Americans and Dr. Baa took the command for what it was, an unmitigated disaster, and were plunged into bitter despondency. They had on hand perhaps $20,000 worth of such drugs, virtually their entire stock, and could hardly expect the U.S. pharmaceutical companies which had donated them to understand why they had had to be destroyed, let alone persuade them to ship out a new batch on very short notice. Yet without their medicines they were less than half a hospital.

"Goddam it," said Al in the midst of the gloom that had settled on all of them, "I say the h-hell with him!"

"No, no," said Baa, appalled at such blasphemy against a minister of the government. "He close hospital. He—he —we must do as he say."

In the end it was Wiedermann who devised the small deceit that saw them safely between the two extremes. "There will be no outdated drugs," he suddenly announced, slamming his fist on the table, "because none of the drugs will be dated!"

Everyone understood at once and chortled in glee and relief. They then spent the night moving the entire supply up to their living quarters, removing the dated labels and returning the vials to their cartons for identification.

These they locked away, each man carrying only enough drugs to the clinic each morning to meet the day's needs. And each man, treasuring the secret, felt frugal, farsighted —and thoroughly virtuous.

Al Harris had never worked harder in his life nor known more genuine contentment. He believed in what he was doing. He could see the results every day and unlike Wiedermann, to whom illness and death were unforgiv able personal foes, Al could even accept the inevitability that they must lose some patients because he was able to fix on the reality that without the Dooley hospital there would be no recoveries, and that half the people who had come there would now be dead.

He believed in his colleagues, too, in Dr. Baa and Reggie Gordon and most of all in Carl Wiedermann. He thought he had never before known so inherently decent a human being as the haggard German with the fiery zeal to help a horde of nameless people with whom he had nothing in common except humanity. It was Wiedermann's devotion to the craft of medicine that first started Al musing about the possibility of someday returning to school to become a doctor.

But that was a long way off. He had committed himself to MEDICO for at least two years, and he thought now that he would serve longer if they wanted him to. When his mother wrote to ask when he would come home and worried about the dangers he faced in a remote corner of the world whose name she couldn't even pronounce, he replied, "Think about it this way, Mom, that I'm really just on the other side of Greenwich Village. I mean if I drilled a hole through the earth at Quang Ngai it would probably come out on Macdougal Street."

Then things began coming unstuck. After Dooley died, the Quang Ngai hospital, like other MEDICO installations, suffered from the sharp conflicts between field forces and New York headquarters.

When Chaney announced the establishment of the Thomas A. Dooley Foundation to take over the MEDICO-administered programs, its proclaimed ambition fired the Quang Ngai contingent with new hope, though they knew that the TADF bank balance was still in Chaney's imagination and its backing remained an open question.

The team began to break up. Bill Gagion was first to go, then Wiedermann had word that his aunt had died and that he would have to return to Italy to settle her estate. Two days before his departure, he wrote Verne Chaney: "I believe in people like you, Verne. I believe in the philosophy of Tom Dooley, for myself first of all, and for the people who need our help. I shall be in Capri waiting to hear from you. If the public response should not be good, if there should be little money, please do not give up hope. Accept this failure if that's what comes, but don't let your enthusiasm fail. Go to Asia for a second trial. I am with you though thousands of miles divide us, and I shall be with you tomorrow and all the days after. *Con affetto,* Carl."

In January, Al Harris's stepfather died and Harris returned to New York to be with his mother. He was restless all the time he was home. He knew Wiedermann had returned from Capri to help Chaney get the Dooley Foundation off the ground and that they'd both gone back to Asia two months before to survey the possibilities. But he waited vainly to hear something from them about a new assignment, stalking the narrow brownstone apartment until even his mother gave up trying to persuade him to stay in New York and wished with him for some word. Once he went uptown to MEDICO headquarters to see Dr. Comanduras, but that turned out badly, too. Comanduras kept saying that field men like Wiedermann and Voulgaropoulos couldn't understand the problems he faced, and that at heart Chaney would always be a field man. Finally Al stood up and said he supposed he would, too, and left.

Chaney called from San Francisco in the second week of February: "You're going to reopen the Dooley hospital at Ban Houei Sai. How soon can you get to the coast?"

"Who's g-going to reopen the hospital at B-Ban Houei Sai?"

"You and Carl. Can you be here day after tomorrow?"

"H-hell, yes."

He borrowed some money from his mother and 48 hours later was sitting in Verne Chaney's apartment fervently listening to an account of the proposed new Dooley programs: the stewardess-volunteers, Tibetan refugee relief, Madame Ngai's An Lac orphanage, and the hospital at Houei Sai. "I've got a Pan Am travel card to give you," Chaney said, "but that's about it. Starting tomorrow I'll be knocking on doors to raise money and I'll send it as soon and as often as it comes to more than the postage. But right now . . ." He held up his empty palms in silent eloquence.

"We'll manage," Al said. "Anyway, I'd a lot s-sooner have my job than yours."

Carl Wiedermann met the plane in Bangkok. He looked fleshless and spent, as always, but there was the exhilaration of the new challenge in his cadaverous black

eyes and he gloated as he steered Al toward a teeming airport bus: "We can't afford taxis any more, old friend.
We're Dooley's coolies now and we have to make the
bahts count."

A *baht*, the Thai monetary unit, is worth about five U.S.
cents, but they treated each one like a gold sovereign.
When they explained their straitened circumstances to a
loyal Dooley supporter from days past, he grandly invited
them to move in with him, and they did. The fact that
he lived at his place of business, a house of ill-fame, did
not deter them in the least, for the arrangements were
forthright: they were to ignore the girls and the goings-
on, then their lodging would be free. They ate one meal
a day on what was left of the money Al's mother had
given him—most of it had gone to buy a typewriter in
Hong Kong—and filled the yearning in their stomachs
with slabs of street vendors' bread and jelly. And each
day they took their high hopes to the American Embassy
to pick up the money Chaney *must* have sent by then, and
returned each day empty-handed and a little more
anxious.

"The typewriter was supposed to be a status symbol," Al
has said. "We were going to send back proper field reports, by damn. But I think we would have hocked it then
and there except that we came up with a very immediate
need for it." Working well into each night, they took turns
writing letters to anyone they could think of who might
contribute some hard cash to the sickly infant called the
Thomas A. Dooley Foundation.

They settled into close friendship during those nervous
days in Bangkok, for they came to understand that the
entire project might stand or fall on the hard decisions
then to be made, and that there was no one but the two

of them to do the deciding. In that time and place, they *were* the Dooley Foundation. And as they lay awake in the steamy nights, Wiedermann told Al the story of how his mother and brother and two sisters had been thrown into a concentration camp by the Nazis, and how at fifteen he had been drafted into the German army. Fleeing toward the Italian border, he was caught and imprisoned and except that the war was nearly over, none of the family would have survived. An uncle, a doctor in the American army, found them and saw that they didn't starve to death.

Wiedermann went to Capri where his aunt lived and later studied medicine at the University of Naples. In 1954, he came to the United States and interned in New York City, then worked at the air base in Thule, Greenland. One May evening in 1960, he sat in a room at Memorial Hospital in Manhattan, vainly trying for a private word as Tom Dooley, undergoing postoperative tests, answered telephone calls, dictated letters and talked with a stream of visitors. All Carl Wiedermann knew for sure was that he had been assigned to a hospital in a place called Quang Ngai.

And now, not two years later, the fate of the thing Tom Dooley had lived and died for rested in his hands, and in those of a young corpsman who still stuttered with inner conflict.

At the end of a week, they knew they would have to make their move, with or without money. Splitting up, they canvassed the medical supply firms in Bangkok and again invoking the charisma of Dooley's name, ordered the medicines and equipment they needed to have. When they had run up charges of some $3,000—"Just send the bill to the Dooley Foundation hospital along with the supplies"—they went out to the airport and hitched a ride with Air America, a commercial line under government contract, first to Vientiane, and finally, on March 10, to Ban Houei Sai.

On the high hill above the east bank of the Mekong River stood the last hospital Tom Dooley ever established. Nearby were the brick and adobe buildings that once served as the French fort, and the lovely old house of the Chaokhoueng, the Governor. Beyond, on the slope and clustered by the river, was the town, a sprawling of bamboo-and-straw huts, and a dusty airstrip.

In October, 1961, MEDICO had closed the hospital down because of what a spokesmen called "instability" in the area. Since then, some American White Star forces, in Laos to train local militia, had lived there but were now long gone and the buildings reeked with the smell of decay; already the unsparing bush reached out to repossess the glade so painfully wrenched from it four years before.

Neither Wiedermann nor Al much noticed the hospital's deterioration. Rehabilitating it was just one more job to add to their lengthening list. Instead, they stood for a long moment, caught, as were all but the most parochial Westerners who came here, by the magnificence of the land's look as it rolled away to the river and past, lusty green to the tops of distant mountains, hushed and unchanging while the great river was a thing of the moment, restless, never the same. For the 50,000 souls who lived within a day's journey of Ban Houei Sai—Lao villagers on the muddy west bank, mountain tribesmen who had fled the communist Pathet Lao—the Mekong was a highway, bathtub, reservoir, laundry and way of life. Only the river and the blue sky led to Ban Houei Sai, or out of it, and in all the years before Dooley came, and in the months since MEDICO had left, there was not a single medical facility in all that remote land of northern Laos.

On the morning of the first day, Wiedermann and Al recruited some White Star soldiers still in the area and went to work cleaning up the neglect of five months. Shortly before dusk they had their first patient, a tribesman with a perforated typhoid ulcer, white with pain. His brother had carried him to the hospital on his back, no one found out how far.

"He needs surgery," Wiedermann dismally decided, "tricky surgery."

There was no waiting for transportation to get him to Vientiane, or even for proper instruments and skilled assistants to arrive. And oppressively aware of his limitations as a surgeon, Wiedermann made the best preparations he could and went again into battle with death, his old and everlasting enemy.

There was no autoclave, so they simply boiled the few scalpels and forceps they found in a cooking pot. Al worked at Wiedermann's side, clamping blood vessels and passing instruments. One White Star man administered anesthesia—open-drop ether—and since there was no electricity and the combination of lantern flame and ether would probably blow them all into oblivion, they pressed another soldier into service to aim a flashlight directly at the incision. But since he kept reeling away in horrified nausea, the illumination remained irregular at best.

The hole in the intestine, the deadly end result of neglected, late-stage typhoid fever, was the size of a fifty-cent piece. Wiedermann dissected the bowel and meticulously cut away the diseased tissue. "Is he still okay?" he kept asking.

And Al, who could be sure only that the man was breathing, replied, "Yes, he's just fine."

The sutures were too big, but there were no others and Wiedermann patiently re-joined the intestine, then closed the wound with the same outsize thread. When the stitching was done, they lay the patient in a corner of the ward— there were no beds yet—gave the brother something to eat and sent him back to the hospital to keep watch. At midnight, they fell onto the wood platforms which were their own beds and sank into exhausted sleep. Only moments later, it seemed, they were awakened by violent pounding on the door of their quarters. It was the brother, soaked, shivering and too wrought up to do more than coax them back to the ward: rain, driven by hurricane-force winds, had flooded it. Their patient lay huddled in soggy misery in his corner, biting cold water splashing in his face.

"Oh, no," Al groaned.

"Grab his feet!" Wiedermann commanded. He was already lifting at the man's armpits.

They carried him up to the house and put him on one of the platforms. They dried him and covered him with all the blankets they could find. Near dawn he fell asleep and the Americans closed their eyes where they sat on the floor and slept, too. The first day at Ban Houei Sai was over.

In the face of a forbidding mortality rate for such surgery even under the best circumstances, the tribesman somehow recovered. And there were other blessings for the new team in Laos. Bit by bit the desperately awaited money began to trickle in from San Francisco. It was years before anyone knew the full story of how tenaciously Chaney worked to raise it, how he would demean himself without flinching for a ten-dollar check. But true to his word, he sent whatever he could lay hands on and like him Wiedermann and Al became expert at fending off financial disaster. They washed bandages and used string when they ran out of surgical tape—but they paid their drug bills. They shopped for food in the riotous Ban Houei Sai morning market and grew their own vegetables. And when there was no gas for the jeep or Vespa, they walked where they had to go. But Wiedermann used to say that "The important thing is that we're here and in business," and they were.

Cleaned up, the barracks-type hospital building was soon filled with patients. Side by side in a single long room bedecked with the vivid red flag of Laos and a framed picture of the king lay sick children, new mothers, medical cases and surgical cases. A week after their sixty beds arrived, the average turnover time between patients was 20 minutes. Each morning at 7 A.M. the walking sick and injured began gathering outside the clinic, and when they had been bandaged and given their pills they went back to their villages and told of the kindness and care they'd had from the *Bac sy my* at the Dooley Foundation hospital. And every few days the line grew noticeably longer.

All through the early spring they had an additional duty—licking envelopes. In the evening they would sit around the table listening to the radio or the record player and stuffing fund appeal letters from the mountainous pile sent to them by San Francisco headquarters for the dramatic effect of a Ban Houei Sai postmark. All told, they sent some 13,500 letters, and the contributions directly attributable to that effort kept the Foundation going through much of 1962.

The two Americans talked often of how useful it would

be to have a second doctor at Ban Houei Sai. Once, when Wiedermann went to Vientiane, Al had to deliver two babies, one in a distant village—a difficult case that, luckily, turned out well. But he was gone for three days and didn't like it. "I don't want to play young Dr. Kildare —I'm not trained for it," he has said. "It scared me. And it scared me to leave the hospital uncovered."

He ached for Wiedermann, too, who had to make countless lonely decisions, so many of them irrevocable, with no one to help confirm a diagnosis, no doctor to whom he could express his doubts. It seemed to Al that this must have troubled the older man profoundly, for his moods tended more and more to melancholy and long silences. And it was clear that the absolutely unending swamp of sickness and the agony of the undeclared war all around them was fraying his nerves raw. "If they sent us ten doctors," he once told Al angrily, "and we were out in the villages every day, and kept the clinic going twenty-four hours, we still couldn't help a tenth of the people who need help, or give them enough food, or clean up the stink that makes them sick in the first place!"

"But those we *do* reach—Carl, it's better than nothing!"

But more and more Wiedermann began to lose faith that it was. Confronted with a sick man or child, he was the same tireless, selfless doctor he'd always been. But at the end of the day, his mind's eye saw not individual patients but a colossal mass of hurt and hungry humans and he came to feel as though he had little more than his compassion to give them, and that it wasn't enough.

Al struggled against the trap of sharing his despondency. He cheered him, argued with him, beguiled him in any way he could conjure up into a return to concerns of the moment. The infallible spur was to challenge him with a difficult case and Al prowled the villages searching them out. Then they'd set off on the Vespa, Wiedermann carrying his bag and hanging on at the back as they bounced over the pocked dirt roads. "Once," Al remembers, "he saw some old guy fishing on the far side of a rice paddy and he made me stop and we went wading across to see what the man had caught. Carl said he loved fishing, but it was people he loved. The old guy was proud as punch that we'd stopped and he held up his sad-looking fish and wanted to give them to us, but Carl told him No thanks. And while they chatted he patched up an ulcerated sore on the old guy's leg, and I don't think I ever thought so much of any man as I did of Carl Wiedermann that day."

In the late spring, they began talking about the possibility of reopening the hospital at Muong Sing, little more than 100 miles north of Houei Sai. The town was still in Royal Army hands but increasing Pathet Lao activity had sent the numbers of battle casualties soaring. It seemed to them important for other reasons. Muong Sing had been Tom Dooley's favorite place on earth and in the minds of Asians and Americans alike remained closely linked with his name. Once the hospital was reestablished, they thought they could leave it in charge of Lao medical aides and make regular visits there to treat the more seriously ill and wounded.

But on Sunday, May 5, news came that Muong Sing had fallen to the Communists three days before. On Monday, the seventh, they had news that Nam Tha had fallen and that communist troops were bearing down on Ban Houei Sai.

There was reason enough for concern—a little road ran directly from Nam Tha to Houei Sai. But the fretful population reacted as though the P.L. would burst into their midst at any moment. Some with boats immediately crossed the river to Chieng Khong in Thailand and next day, when the first refugees began straggling in with word that the Royal Army was falling back and abandoning weapons and wounded, a kind of hysteria seized the town and nearly everyone in it. Shopkeepers and peasants fled to the river and scrambled and fought for places in the boats, while the Chaokhoueng and his retinue and a handful of others with money and station flew on the last planes to Vientiane and Luang Prabang, the ancient royal capital.

That night, Tuesday, May 8, no one at the Dooley hospital on the hill slept, for the first wounded began to arrive and, as Wiedermann put it, "There were surgical interventions of from moderate to severe gravity for nine hours." The hot orange glow of distant forest fires hung in the black sky, and some said they were lit by tribespeople to guide the P.L. and others said that villagers were burning homes and land in order to deny the enemy any shred of comfort.

By Wednesday, Houei Sai was in chaos. Every street and roadway disgorged its clots of refugees on the riverbank, already aswarm with the last of the town's civilians, disparate packs of belongings at their feet and on their backs, clamoring to be taken across to the safety of Thailand. The local military pushed their way through the crowd with demolition charges for every substantial building. Royal Army soldiers, dazed with defeat and glassy-eyed from the fatigue of three days of forced marching, wandered pointlessly about and finally found their way to the river too and overloaded the small boats. And one capsized just opposite the airstrip, its occupants trapped by the hard-running Mekong and by their heavy gear and their exhaustion, and thirty-five drowned. But no one in the town had yet seen a Pathet Lao.

That night, badgered by the military and pressed by rumors that the P.L. were close—50, 30, even 10 kilometers away—Wiedermann and Al decided they would have to evacuate the hospital. They borrowed a jeep from the military and began at once to move supplies and surgical equipment down to the river. In the morning, Wiedermann crossed over to Chieng Khong and arranged with Thai authorities to set up an emergency hospital in the vacant ground floor of a government building on the river road. All that day they moved patients and medical stores across the Mekong and were well enough established by midnight to perform urgent surgery on a Thai shot on the Houei Sai side for looting. Early on Friday morning, Al set out alone, the last man to go back, to salvage some blankets, splints and orthopedic instruments. He had to pay a frightened Thai boatman 1,000 *bahts*, about $50, for the privilege.

From the tangled babble on the west bank—women dragging children and belongings through the mud; men struggling to shove dead horses, drowned in crossing, out from the ensnaring bush so they would float downstream and loose their stench on some other village—Al climbed onto the dock of a deserted town. Only the military were left in Ban Houei Sai, abstracted and glum as they charged through the work of demolition. The Chaokhoueng's house blew up with a dusty roar just as Al reached the top of the hill, and all he could see of the graceful white building when the pulverized plaster and stone settled was the truncated entrance pavilion. The military commander's quarters went next, and other buildings in the town.

Al ran the last 150 yards to the hospital. A troop of soldiers was rolling a length of fuse wire toward the main building and, panting and furiously angry, he cried out, "Hey! Wait a minute! Nobody's blowing up that goddam hospital!"

They looked at him in confusion, and one said in English: "We are ordered to. The orders are to blow everything on hill."

"Listen, goddam it, have you seen any P.L.? C-can't you wait till you know where they are before you demolish every worthwhile building in Houei Sai? You've got people on the Nam Tha road—when *they* see P.L. you'd be able to blow the whole town up and still have time to *swim* across the goddam river."

"We have orders."

Al conferred a loud obscenity on their orders. He was now full of this helpless rage, wildly scouring his mind for some way to save the hospital, when the town's Catholic priest, an old Lao, came over the brow of the hill on his bicycle, pumping furiously toward the town. "Father!" he called out. "Father, for God's sake, will you help me?"

The priest swerved toward them. Sweat poured from his wrinkled old face and his cassock was wet all down the back and gray with dust.

"Father," Al pleaded, "can't you please tell these l-lunkheads not to blow up the hospital? There are no P.L. here. They may not ever come here. Why the hell . . .?"

"I have told them," the old man said wearily. "They wanted to destroy the church and I sent two parishioners up the Nam Tha road and they went 20 kilometers and saw no one but Royal Army soldiers. But they destroyed the church anyway. They did not listen."

"They'll listen now," Al said at last, "or they'll have a hell of a dead American on their hands. Because I'm going into that hospital and I'm not coming out until they take their dynamite away or prove to me that Houei Sai is really going down the drain."

He stalked up the steps of the hospital and slammed the door behind him. The soldiers stood stunned for a moment, then broke into an argument with the priest and a more rancorous one among themselves. But in the end they rolled up their wire and went away, and Al Harris let loose a long, shuddering breath. "I decided that I wasn't going to get blown up right away," he has said. "Now all I had to worry about was the P.L."

But he had been right about the P.L. in the first place. He stayed four days and none appeared and hour by hour the sense of imminent doom lifted from the town. On the third day, a young monk came up the hill and said he was sick, and though Al couldn't find anything wrong with him he was happy to admit him to the hospital. "He kept calling for food or a bedpan or some other damn thing and, hell, he was healthier than I was. But I fetched for him. I was glad for the company."

On Tuesday, May 15, the soldiers came to take the demolition charges away and that afternoon Al began hauling bedding and supplies down to the river, returning to Chieng Khong in a boat packed to the gunwales. In the cramped and dingy improvised hospital he found Carl Wiedermann and the Lao assistants still working stoically away on refugees, fresh battle casualties brought downstream, and on ever-increasing numbers of sick Thais, grateful to have the Dooley Foundation hospital on their side of the river. In fact, Wiedermann reported, Thai officials had sounded him out about staying permanently.

But their place was in Houei Sai. They would keep emergency facilities in Chieng Khong, but they meant to return to Laos as soon as the military situation stabilized and the Health Ministry gave approval. As it turned out, this took a special trip to Vientiane by Wiedermann and not until May 24—when nearly all the civilian population of Houei Sai had already returned—were they allowed back.

With still a long way to go. They had lost nearly all their personal belongings and kitchen supplies to looters and it was two weeks before the hospital and quarters were clean. And just five days after they were finally reorganized and again functioning normally, another Pathet Lao attack, close enough this time so they could hear the snapping rifle fire, drove them back to Chieng Khong. This time they stayed only three days, but the tremendous emotional and physical effort to reestablish themselves once more drained their spirits.

Early in June Al flew to Vientiane to buy supplies, and on the tenth Wiedermann wrote a long letter to Chaney summarizing the dismal events of the past month. As he wrote, the record player to which he had been listening broke down and he noted this in the letter, adding, "Strange, but there are times when so much goes wrong that everything looks impossibly blue."

Al got a ride back on the Air America milk run to the northern villages and came within 5,000 feet of making it to Houei Sai in time. But as they dipped in for the landing a sudden mist rolled up the river and completely obscured the airstrip, and the pilot had to turn back to Vientiane. Next morning Al went to Luang Prabang hoping to catch a flight from there to Houei Sai. But sometime in that 24-hour period, Carl Wiedermann shot himself through the head and spattered that fine brain all over the west wall of the quarters.

The nightmare of the next days became scrambled with implacable realities. Al had to make the arrangements to have Wiedermann's remains shipped to the States; to answer the endless questions of American Embassy officials who came running to Houei Sai immediately after the tragedy—but had never thought to come before—to make a long, sad report to Chaney; to sec the patients who came without end since sickness didn't end on the Mekong because Wiedermann was dead. So he did all the things that needed to be done, sometimes stupefied with grief, sometimes blindly angry with himself for not having been there when his friend needed him, and every moment achingly aware that his world would never be the same without Carl Wiedermann in it. "I thought at first 1 might have a nervous breakdown," he wrote Chaney near the end of June, then added wryly, "but I find I can't work this into my schedule."

Worst of all was the awful loneliness. Sometimes when he worked he could lose himself in the mechanics of medicine, the needs of his patients, the rote and rhythm of what he'd been doing for two years. But at night there was no way to escape the nagging, brooding things that came into his head and wouldn't go away, no way to pretend that anything at all was the same.

And now all the solitary decisions were his and sometimes he didn't know what to do. Once they brought him a man who'd been gored by a water buffalo, his front laid open from left hip bone to right shoulder. "I panicked,"

Al has since said. "I wanted to run away. I wanted to tell them to take that bloody mess with its exposed guts the hell out of my hospital, because I didn't know what to do."

But of course he did what had to be done. He went out on the steps and took deep breaths, then ordered the man to the operating room and began to sew. Three hours, hundreds of stitches and two pints of blood later, he came out again, chalky and lightheaded and not at all certain that he wasn't going to be sick after all. But he had done the job and the patient lived.

Chaney wrote that in spite of the most intensive effort, he was still not able to say when a doctor could be sent to Houei Sai. But in July, Reggie Gordon came and having his old colleague back with him did much to lift Al's spirits. And Reggie's return turned out to be providential, for later that summer Al Harris's mother died and once again he had to go home on the saddest mission.

He didn't think much about what he'd do beyond the next few days; the past was still very much with him. One thing he did *not* want to do, he'd lately found, was to study medicine. There had been too many long, late-at-night talks with Wiedermann about their practicing together. He felt now that without the older man's encouragement he could never attain his level of skill and compassion, and he didn't want to try. He wrote Chaney, "But I will never lose the love I have for Asia so maybe I can find some kind of work out there."

Then two important things happened to Al Harris. First, he met a girl named Barbara, dark-haired and lovely, and for the first time in his life the notion of getting married came poking into his head. But there were dark hours when the idea seemed outlandish: Barbara was a very special girl and he was the most ordinary of young men, with no background, no promise and only some vague fantasy about going back to Asia to offer her. And he didn't dare.

The second thing was another of those telephone calls from Verne Chaney, with whom he had been in sporadic touch all year. The Foundation was taking hold in Laos, Chaney said. A doctor and three nurses were now at Ban Houei Sai and agreement had been reached to provide American staff for the 200-bed hospital at Pakse, and for a smaller one at Khong, near the Cambodian border. "We need somebody in charge of the whole operation in Laos now, Al, an administrative field director. How about it?"

"Me?"

"Yes."

Al thought that over for a long moment. He said, "Verne, I want to do it, you know that. But I don't have that kind of experience. I'm an aide man. I fix cuts and pass out aspirins. You're offering this to me out of loyalty or sentiment."

"You're about half right," Chaney promptly responded. "But if I had a better-qualified man I'd send him. I don't. Not one with your guts anyway."

A week later Al was back in San Francisco for three days of briefing—and a lot of thinking about Barbara. And the night before he flew off for Hong Kong, Saigon and Vientiane, he telephoned her long-distance and said he had a kind of wild life to offer her—uncertain quarters; long separations; and an income, when it was available, of $150 a month—but that he loved her and would she come to Vientiane and be his wife? And without hesitation she said she would and not long after she followed him to Asia and they were married.

It was a wild life indeed. To begin with, they moved into the Constellation Hotel, "for only a few days," Al promised in all innocence. Two months later they were still there, for decent housing was hard to find in Vientiane and invariably required more cash in advance than ever seemed to be available for that purpose in the Dooley Foundation coffers. "Each time we did have enough money set by," Barbara says, "we also had a crisis to go with it—a broken generator at Houei Sai, a new motor needed for the boat at Khong—and of course those things had a higher priority than staff quarters."

And so with Al away three weeks of every month visiting hospitals and trying to set up new Foundation programs, his bride had a lonely hotel honeymoon. For company she could choose between the old Asia hands—American reporters, French teachers and German engineering consultants—who drank briskly at the Constellation bar and in doom-tinged voices forecast *coups d'état* and chaos, and the inevitable retinue of pimps, prostitutes and opium smugglers strewn through the hotels of the Far East. Her choice was hardly surprising: "I never came out of my room except to eat. They must have thought I was crazy, but they scared the life out of me."

Meanwhile Al was having his own troubles. "It was this crazy hybrid feeling about Dooley: the Lao thought he was the greatest American who ever lived and the Americans in Laos thought he was the biggest bastard who ever had. He'd stepped on a lot of feet in his time, hard. Dooley never went politely up the chain of command. He had cancer and was in a hurry. When he needed something he went right to the Ambassador or the director of

USAID. Naturally this made all the second and third assistants sore and the one thing they were good at was holding a grudge. So when I came along with my big smile and that fancy title, Dooley Foundation Administrative Field Director, I naturally inherited all Tom Dooley's enemies."

Their revenge was more petty than substantial—a denial of commissary privileges to the Foundation, unaccountable delays in granting its members space on otherwise empty planes—but these irritations, dumped on top of his major worries, sometimes made Al feel like charging up to the Embassy compound and bashing heads. But he didn't.

"I realize, Verne," he had written Chaney early on, "that in sending me to Laos as administrative field director you are taking a hell of a chance because of my limited capabilities. But I can't tell you enough times how important it is for Al Harris to be successful, not for me, but because if I fail I'd be hurting you and the Foundation. I'll tell you this, old buddy—if I do louse up, I'll come home at my own expense."

He has said, too, that he meant to think out every decision. And thinking out the impasse with minor officialdom in Laos he came to the conclusion that fence-mending, not head-bashing, was called for. So mend fences he did, and in a surprisingly short time Foundation members had high priority for air transportation on a "space available" basis, though Barbara would continue to shop at the morning market along with half the Lao housewives in Vientiane.

But she had a house! In March, the happy confluence of events—enough cash and the availability of a reasonably comfortable place—finally occurred and the Harrises moved in forthwith, along with a cook, a maid, three stewardesses and a nurse en route to Dharamsala, India. For it was clearly understood that while the house on a quiet street near the airport would be home to Al and Barbara, it was also Dooley Foundation headquarters in Laos and had to serve as temporary quarters for a steady stream of staffers passing through Vientiane and awaiting transportation home or to any of the far-flung Foundation outposts in Southeast Asia. How did Barbara like *that*?

"What can I say? Most of these people were great and I hated to see them go just after we'd become friends. But we're all human and have our little quirks and they're bound to come out when you're rubbing elbows with people you never laid eyes on until twenty minutes ago, using the same bathroom—with an Asian john!—eating together and having to plot for half an hour of privacy."

One girl would eat nothing but peanut butter—a jar a day! Another said she'd be constipated if she didn't have dinner by 5:30, although after the long afternoon heat no one else felt like eating much before 7. "That was a new one on me," Al recalls. "I never heard a Westerner in Asia worrying about being *constipated*."

And then, of course, there were the simple mechanics of housekeeping in a land where the amenities, such as they were, could never be taken for granted. "I'm a New Yorker," Barbara says ruefully. "I grew up believing that electricity was your *right*, a sort of God-given gift from Consolidated Edison. If you wanted water you turned the tap and if water didn't come you phoned the company and yelled. In Vientiane there was no company, which was probably for the best because in our house there was no telephone."

Al's problems teetered above his head throughout his two-year tour as area administrator, periodically threatening to come crashing down on him, undoing the program in Laos, burying the entire Dooley Foundation. As always, financial disaster was rarely farther than a day's mail behind him. He thought nothing about the months when his token salary wasn't paid—nor did any of the staff—but they did have to eat and pay rent, and there were essential drugs and supplies needed in the field installations. So the checks from San Francisco were fervently awaited and when they didn't come everyone turned to Al Harris with the unspoken question loud on their stricken faces—"What'll we do *now*?" And before long he learned to swallow his own panic, smile and say, "Why, we'll wait for tomorrow's mail."

Whenever there was a little extra money, he liked to give some to the men in the remote stations and send them into Vientiane or Bangkok to let their hair down, as Dooley had done. Now, with two years at close quarters in Quang Ngai and Houci Sai behind him, Al vividly understood how therapeutic a few days of bustle and bright lights could be. "What else is there for a guy in some boondocks hospital? He lives with misery, works God knows how many hours a day and can't even raise a little hell in town because you just don't do that sort of thing around your own flagpole, not with the P.L. all over the place and sure to spread it up and down the river about what a bunch of bums the Dooley Americans are."

Once a young corpsman, taken aback by Al's directive to let off some steam in Bangkok for a few days—and stunned by the 2,000 *kip*, about $5, that went with it—asked if he couldn't use the money instead to buy his mother a birthday present. "Son," said Al, perhaps two

years the corpsman's senior, "I certainly wish your mother
a happy birthday, and many more. But your mother isn't
my responsibility. You are. So you just be on that milk
run out of here this afternoon and don't come back without a hangover."

They went through two *coups*. The first one merely kept
them up all night with a spectacular display of bomb
bursts and the clatter of machine-gun fire. The second
began promptly at 8 A.M., February 3, 1965—just minutes
after Al had taken off for Pakse and Khong Island. "The
co-pilot came back to tell us they were fighting like hell
just below and I said he had to by God turn back, my wife
was down there. But he just smiled and went back up
front and that airplane never changed course till we were
over Pakse."

There Dr. Alex del Carmen, a longtime friend of the
Dooley Foundation, got Al aboard a flight to Nong Khai,
Thailand, across the Mekong from Vientiane, where some
money and his incessant pleas finally persuaded a boatman
to ferry him over around 6 P.M. Then he started walking. The capital of Laos looked abandoned, but it was
evident that there were plenty of people about by the
nervous way shutters opened a crack, then closed tight
again, and by the challenges flung at him from behind the
barricades every block or so. "I didn't know if they were
good guys or bad guys. I just hollered back that I was
American in every language I knew and kept walking."

Artillery shells, fired from some place beyond the
USAID compound, were still crumping into the littered
streets. The Pan American Building and the police sta-

tion were demolished. And Al had graphic visions of Barbara huddled in terror somewhere without even anyone to tell her what was happening, and he broke into a trot. At the Constellation Hotel he pounded on the door until they let him in, and his knees sagged at the spectacle:

"There must have been two hundred people behind that big concrete bar, half of them plastered or working at it, the other half scared silly by the shooting outside. I asked somebody if they'd seen my wife, Barbara Harris, and there was this big, wailing, 'Ye-e-ess!' from behind the bar, a flash of white dress as she came flying at me, and then she was draped around my neck and hanging on for dear life. So we found us a spot on the floor and waited until morning when the government had settled its little differences. Then we went back to work."

Early in 1966, Chaney wrote to say that he had found a young man named Jack Hjelt who would be coming out soon with his wife and baby daughter to take over as administrative field director, and the Harrises moodily prepared to return home. "We'd have stayed forever," Al now says, "but it's not that kind of world, is it? I was nearly thirty years old and it was time to start thinking about making some money and raising a family."

Chances are they'll go back. As Al studies toward his degree and works as a hospital technician, his feelings about the work of the Dooley Foundation are as strong as ever. "It's the best and cheapest way there is to sell America in Asia," he says unequivocally. He is a member of the New York chapter's board of directors and seems to relive his field days whenever he talks about them.

And what has he, Al Harris, gotten out of the four years he gave to Tom Dooley's tenacious idea? He shrugs, grins at the brand-new daughter in the circle of his arm, then shrugs again. "I don't know," he finally says. "I'm not so hot talking about the self-realization stuff."

And so he never mentioned that it has been years since he stuttered.

CHAPTER III

Quang Ngai

BARBARA BOYD, WHO NEVER really got over what Tom Dooley said to her by the side of a hotel swimming pool in Bangkok the year she was nineteen, was predisposed to the ministry of service without knowing it. Long before, when her father was supervising the construction of a dam in the remote hill country of Haiti, something happened that fixed itself on her young girl's mind and never went away. Driving one day along a twisting little road near the Dominican border with her parents and her brother, she saw a small girl and an old lady by the edge of a sugar-cane field and the girl's right arm was wrapped in a banana leaf and dripping blood. When she mentioned this to her father he stopped the car and got out. Soon the others got out too and they stood on the dusty road, the four scrubbed Americans, and the sad old Haitian woman and her sad little granddaughter.

Three weeks before, the child's arm had been caught in a cane crusher. They had treated it with cow dung and herbs, as was their way, but it did not get better. Now it hurt very badly, the grandmother said, and the child could not sleep and whimpered through the night.

77

Tom Boyd gently took the banana leaf off. His family turned away in horror, but he stared in helpless rage at the mangled arm, its wounds still bloody raw and putrid with infection. He had worked in the backwoods of the world and knew well the inevitable progression of an existence that was spawned in poverty, lived in ignorance, and ended so often in the most appalling suffering. But every time he saw it anew he was taken with this same anger because he was that kind of man.

He brought his canteen and a first aid kit from the car. He cleaned the arm and put Merthiolate on it, then wrapped it in clean bandages. "In seven days," he told the grandmother in the French patois that was the native language of the hill people, "bring the child back to this place in the road and I will change the dressing again. Meanwhile let no one else touch the arm."

Barbara returned with her father that appointed Sunday, and a group of five or six from their village came with the old woman and the child. The next week there were more people, and still more the next. They came, these innocents, many of whom had never seen a white man and none of whom had ever even heard of one troubling over one of them, because they simply could not believe what the grandmother told them. And seeing, they could hardly believe it yet.

In the end, the girl's arm proved too far gone for Tom Boyd to restore with only his simple treatments and he had to take her to Port-au-Prince for surgery. But had he never chanced along that little back road, there would have been no possibility of saving the arm at all, and perhaps not much of saving that child's life. And this is the thing that clung to his daughter's mind, that among the world's dispossessed and downtrodden majority, it doesn't take much to help a very great deal.

So though she could resist Dooley's peremptory summons to go to work in one of his hospitals when they met that day in Bangkok, though she could tell him—and mean it—that she was going to go back to the States and have fun like a *normal* nineteen-year-old, the seed of his idea fell on fertile ground. She did have fun, but she didn't forget him, and she didn't forget the unending need of the people he'd talked about because she had seen the need with her own eyes.

Sometimes she talked about Dooley and his work to the two doctors she worked for in Dallas. They didn't understand. They didn't understand how a man could drudge through eight, ten, twelve years of medical training, then give up all the creature comfort his hard-earned skills could buy to go live in a jungle. They didn't understand why a man should want to take the most meticulous professional preparation and invest it in a sea of misery where it could scarcely be felt. "What kind of medicine is it anyway? What kind of equipment can he have out there?" one said. "How can he keep up with all the new drugs and techniques?"

Barbara didn't know the answers. She only knew that the need was greater where Dooley was, that though he might never eliminate tuberculosis or typhoid fever in Laos, what little he could do was vastly important and infinitely better than if no one did anything at all. But she was young and her employers were imposing and successful and she couldn't explain her feelings to them.

"The thing is," she has since said, "they were thoroughly decent men. They saw clinic patients regularly and charged nothing and if they had come across someone

bleeding on the street, or in pain, they'd have done anything to help. But giving their private patients careful
individual attention—that was what medicine meant to
them."

But they were good-natured about it. They used to say,
"If you want to take off for some Asian jungle, good luck.
We're staying in Dallas." And one day she knew that's
what she had to do. She had to live up to that unspoken
promise to herself. So she quit her job and went to New
York, and though Dooley died before she could get to see
him, she called Dr. Peter Comanduras at MEDICO and
in January, 1962, bought a ticket to Saigon. She would
visit her parents there—her father was now working on a
Vietnamese water system—and have a good talk with Dr.
James Luce, who had by then replaced Carl Wiedermann,
about the hospital at Quang Ngai. Still, her first instinct
was to return to Haiti, where MEDICO was operating a
hospital. But as it happened, Dr. Jim Luce of Quang Ngai
was in Saigon to buy supplies and Barbara's talk with him
turned into a commitment.

"Everyone wants to go to the Caribbean—it's so handy
to home," he said to her. "But if you really feel like doing
something, come back to Quang Ngai with me now. We're
starting an immunization program there that could change
the health profile of the entire province."

She was moved by his earnest way of saying things, by
the simple and straightforward appeal for her help. "All
right," she said abruptly. "How do I get to Quang Ngai?"

Luce got her a seat on a U.S. air force plane. The crew
made much of the fact that they flew this run every two
weeks or so and one said, "We'll save space for you next
time out. You'll be ready to come back by then."

"Want to bet?" she answered.

They did not, and so saved themselves some money. For Barbara loved Quang Ngai from the minute the C-123 set down—the lonely little shack at the end of the strip that was all the air terminal there was; the glistening green rice paddies on both sides of the town; and the small, neatly kept hospital compound that plainly reflected the medical team's profound feeling for it. The staff consisted of Jim Luce; the surgeon, Dr. José Castellanos; Ed Wilson, a male nurse from Ireland by way of Texas; Marcella O'Connor, a fine surgical nurse who'd come to Asia on the hospital ship *Hope* and had planned to return by driving, walking or taking a bus to India, then Africa, until she, too, ran into Luce's formidable persuasion in Saigon; and three Vietnamese interpreters.

"They didn't know what to make of me," Barbara remembers, "a young American stewardess turning up that way—unannounced, inexperienced and sort of open-mouthed about the whole thing. I think they were pretty sure I wouldn't last long either."

But Barbara well remembered Dooley's unbending prerequisite—"I send people who will stay!"—and she had every intention of staying. She had had some nursing training and knew she needed more. But she also knew that Quang Ngai would be the most valuable teacher of all. "You learn what you need to know in the field because you have to. There's nobody else to do your job." So she was soon assisting on major surgery—though she'd never been in an operating room before—and treating all sorts of ills in the villages of the province, convinced, as were all the old Dooley hands, that the best-trained doctors and nurses in the world would not be much use if they came at great expense to MEDICO and promptly began thinking about the next plane home.

Army doctors and USAID officials came to look at their facilities. Almost without exception, their reaction was dismay and their first question was something like, "My God, how can you manage with—this?" And Dr. Luce or Dr. Castellanos would try to explain that they managed quite well, that what they had was a vast improvement over what was there when they came, and infinitely better than what Carl Wiedermann and Al Harris first found at Quang Ngai two years before. But the visitors, accustomed to superb military hospitals like Walter Reed and Tripler General, would tick off all the facilities and equipment and personnel that were missing at Quang Ngai, never understanding that in fact there was very little that could be done differently, and they left shaking their heads.

The hospital was always full. There were forty beds and an average of sixty medical and surgical patients, an aggregate made possible by the expedient of putting more then one patient in a bed. In fact, when V.C. activity was high, three in a bed was not uncommon and was referred to by the nurses as a semi-private accommodation. The isolation ward was usually crowded with typhoid cases, and the separate TB building with a combination of patients for whom they held out some real hope and those for whom there was none. The great majority of tuberculars were still being treated at the clinic and sent home.

But of all the programs at Quang Ngai, the one that raised staff hopes highest was the plan to immunize children against diphtheria, whooping cough and tetanus. Dr.

Luce, stirred by the high incidence of these killer diseases, had made an arrangement with USAID, which had a large supply of the DPT vaccine on hand but had been able to immunize only a few hundred children in Saigon, and with the Vietnamese Minister of Health: if USAID would provide the vaccine, Dooley teams of American and Vietnamese would undertake to immunize as many children in Quang Ngai province between the ages of one and six as they could reach. This effort was to be considered a pilot program and, if successful, extended to other provinces.

It was a formidable undertaking. Quang Ngai wasn't much bigger than Rhode Island but it was cut by mountains and a rugged coast and had long been a Viet Cong strongpoint. But the Vietnamese health technicians worked out a timetable of village visits and each day Barbara and Marcella O'Connor, heading separate teams, struck out for the hinterlands. They drove two palsied trucks or the rattling jeep, and they went places no other Westerner had ever been. And thanks to the posters and placards with which they flooded the countryside to explain the immunization program and list the date each village would be visited, they were awaited by an invariable phalanx of mothers, some of whom had walked 50 kilometers from the deepest bush, all thrusting toward the school building or wooden hut where the Dooley team was set up, all towing at least one small child.

"When the jet injectors were working, we had a fighting chance to keep some semblance of a line moving," Barbara recalls. "But once they broke down and we had to take time to boil needles and syringes, the people began knocking down doors and climbing in the windows."

The jet injector—there were two, also borrowed from

USAID—worked electrically and built up a head of pressure that squirted the three-in-one shot right through the skin without a needle and could empty a ten-injection vial as fast as an arm could be stuck in front of it. For as long as they worked they were a blessing, well worth the two teams' ritualistic effort each morning of heaving the ponderous electric generators aboard the trucks. The trouble was that no jet injector anywhere had ever been put to such intensive usage and after 5,000 shots both broke down and were thereafter frequently out of action for repairs. The teams then used disposable injection units for as long as they lasted, finally switching to glass syringes and needles that had to be boiled for twenty minutes after each shot, meaning they were forced to carry some 300 of each on every trip.

But day by day they moved farther out into the province, sometimes wheedling helicopter rides from the military when they were bound for remote districts. And everywhere it was the same—hundreds of women and children, all laughing with irrepressible good humor, all cheerfully thrusting elbows, shoulders and hips toward the harried medics. Once Luce had a narrow wooden chute built, hoping it would force patients and parents into line before they reached the nurses, and Barbara dutifully helped hoist it up on the truck. Still smiling, the women tore it to pieces in ten minutes. Yet notwithstanding the chaos, every child was somehow registered, every parent given a card to present for the second injection and the third. And despite the hard distances and the necessarily random publicity given to subsequent village visits, nearly 90 per cent of the children who got the first shot got all three in the series.

"Nothing remotely like this had ever happened to these

people before," Barbara says. "If you told them about a fine road built with American dollars it had no meaning for them. They had no cars. They'd shrug and tell you they'd been walking the paddies and riverbanks all their lives and what was wrong with that? But when you come into their villages with medicine they begin to have some feeling for American aid. Maybe they had no idea what diseases we were immunizing against, but they very well knew that their children died from them."

For nine grueling months, the Dooley staff lived the immunization program from first light to dark each day. Evenings were most typically devoted to the repair of a truck, generator or the water pump, all of which Barbara describes as having been "abandoned here by Moses on his way to the Promised Land." Since none of the medical personnel was mechanically apt, their main effort was expended persuading the army, air force, USAID—or whichever other unit chanced to be in the vicinity—to loan them someone who was.

The truck she drove had lost its floorboards on some long-forgotten excursion. One day it slithered on the one-lane road, climbed a four-foot embankment and settled itself—seemingly forever—so deep in a rice paddy that water came lapping at her ankles. The Vietnamese nurse with her, accustomed to catastrophe, had thoughtfully raised her feet to the dashboard and so salvaged her shoes when she stepped out into the paddy.

"Today I found out what two nurses do when they run their truck into a rice paddy," Barbara wrote her parents that night. "They push it out."

They had to rebuild a section of road before they did, shoveling a stretch of embankment down under their tires and spewing mud and muck into the sky as they gunned the motor, pushed, gunned some more.

The Viet Cong were much a part of their daily lives. The hospital had its regular quota of battle casualties and not infrequently one of the immunization teams would drive into a village where the chief or an elder had just been assassinated. But all the Dooley staff wore white uniforms and their trucks had bright red crosses and they made no secret of their comings and goings. Says Barbara:

"How could we hide? We had to let the people know when we were coming to a village—we advertised it. I think the V.C. knew every time we blew our nose. But they never hurt us."

Still, as long as they were in an area that then had more Viet Cong than ARVN (Army of the Republic of Vietnam) and U.S. forces combined, what applied yesterday was no guarantee of what might happen tomorrow, and all hands felt the same unease along the lonely stretches or when the sun started to redden and sink. In September, 1962, the newly formed Vietnamese 25th Division and their 100-odd American advisers moved into a compound not far from Quang Ngai town and at once V.C. activity flared. The Communists were being pinched by the ARVN troops and they wanted everyone in Quang Ngai province to feel their displeasure. The casualty rate rose dramatically, mainly among civilians, and the Dooley hospital had a headlong rush of mine, grenade and bayonet injuries.

Understaffed and underequipped for these emergencies, the medical personnel lost track of their on-duty hours and, in the best spirit of Dooley himself, scrounged far and wide for the things they had to have. Most critically needed was an autoclave large enough to sterilize instruments and surgical packs, along with the spate of syringes used in the immunization program. The little French unit they had was simply not adequate for their suddenly increased requirements, but nowhere could they pry loose a replacement. Then one day Barbara learned from an American helicopter pilot based at Da Nang, 70 miles up the coast, that an army field hospital had recently been established there, and a solution seemed in sight.

"Let me fly back with you, all right?" she said, and a few hours later was prowling through the immaculate military compound looking for the doctor in charge.

He turned out to be a young captain (who will here remain unnamed for obvious reasons), new to Vietnam and somewhat startled to be abruptly confronted by an attractive nurse who came directly to the point of her visit. In three or four pithy sentences she told him where she was from and what her problem was. Then she asked, "Do you have an extra autoclave?"

"Yes," he said, "I have two."

"Can you give me one for Quang Ngai?" She held her breath.

"No, I couldn't do that. They're signed out to me and there'd be red tape clear back to Washington if I *gave* one away." Barbara turned to the door in disappointment. "But I'm going to be here for a year and there's no reason I can't *lend* you one until I leave."

She would have kissed him except that they were being scrutinized by every patient and orderly on the floor. So she thanked him from the bottom of her heart and flew off with a great gleaming new autoclave, to be welcomed with appropriate acclamation at Quang Ngai.

Nor was that the last of the young captain's benefactions. He was plainly moved by what the Dooley staff was trying to do and in the months to come he sent them all the equipment and medicine he could spare. When he got a ten-day leave he gave that to them, too, accompanying Luce on village rounds and assisting at clinics and surgery. And that was *his* reward. "I've learned more in these ten days than I could have gotten out of a whole year's course in parasitic medicine," he told them when he left. By the time his tour of duty was up and the autoclave had to be returned, they had finally "liberated" one from USAID.

None of them, least of all Barbara, could get used to the stoic way the Vietnamese accepted death, dying and the excruciating backlash of war. They had set up a rural health clinic perhaps 20 kilometers from the hospital, and here Barbara came one noon, all innocence, to conduct an immunization clinic. "There had been a nasty little battle the night before," she remembers, "the local militia trying to stand off the V.C. until the ARVN troops got there. But the ARVN troops didn't come until it was all over, just in time in fact, to cart away the dead and patch up the lightly wounded."

Between the two was a frightened little farmer, shot twice through the upper arm and quietly bleeding to death. Some militiamen had brought him to the clinic hours before, but until Barbara arrived there was no one to do anything and so he lay on the bare ground in the hot sun, in the smell of his own fear, and he whitened and his eyes began to roll vacantly. Even as Barbara pressed surgical packs to the oozing holes in his arm, he went into shock and began dying.

"I need something warm to wrap him in!" she cried. Someone brought a tattered blanket and she wound it twice around the wasted little body, meanwhile snapping out instructions for an immediate return to the hospital. "Why didn't the ARVN people bring him in hours ago?" she said angrily. "They have ambulances. This man could have been on his way home now instead of"—she pointed to the pathetic figure on the ground, breath rattling raggedly in his throat—"this!"

"We ask them to," one of the militiamen told her. "We beg them. But they say no, they have no orders to go Quang Ngai."

She hadn't time to do more than swallow her fury. She ordered the wounded Vietnamese placed in a chair in the back of the jeep station wagon, tilted well back so some blood would get to his head, and held by the two militiamen and Luke, her interpreter. Then she leaped behind the wheel and flung them all down Route 1, a pinched little road strewn with ruts, carts, and an occasional water buffalo, at 60 miles an hour, siren shrieking a warning over the hushed countryside. Regularly the desperately hurt farmer let loose a great shuddering gasp and quit breathing, and Luke squeezed his narrow chest and blew into his mouth until some small spark of life again took hold.

As they came wailing up from the south to the only highway intersection in Quang Ngai town—Barbara steeled to make the screeching, two-wheel left turn toward the hospital—a military convoy coming down from the north had already begun a lumbering turn in that same direction.

"Damn, damn, double-damn!" she said aloud and hit the brakes.

But a minor miracle in the person of a Quang Ngai policeman saw them through. Recognizing the Dooley hospital jeep, he dashed to the center of the intersection, stuck his palm out at the next military vehicle in line and shooed the improvised ambulance safely around the corner. As it happened, the occupant of that vehicle was the commander-in-chief of the Vietnamese First Corps, a general who would head one of the juntas that ruled Vietnam between the death of President Diem and the election in 1967. Curious to know what urgent matter had held him up, the general ordered his driver to pull out of the convoy and follow the jeep.

Barbara came tearing into the hospital compound with the siren still screaming. Luce and José Castellanos ran out of the surgery with dextrose and saline solution and were feeding it into the wounded man's veins even as the other Vietnamese were lifting him out. "And me," Barbara recalls, "I was still so mad that I could chew nails and was telling everyone in earshot—and that must have covered a country mile—that that poor guy was dying because some ARVN troops refused to bring him in here."

It was about this time that the Vietnamese general stepped out of his car and walked over to join the group around the incensed American nurse, who had yet to pause for breath. Except that she had happened along, she was saying, the poor farmer would have lain out there untended until he'd bled to death. Nor was this the only instance of the army's cruel indifference to suffering: they had ambulances and here was a hospital; why wouldn't they bring their wounded in?

By this time the general had finally gotten close enough to be heard. "I beg your pardon," he said to her in faultless English, "could you tell me just what the trouble is?"

"Sure I'll tell you!" And she did, repeating her fiery discourse, adding the fact that though their hospital was short of people and equipment and space, they were in

Vietnam to save lives and the Vietnamese had to help them. Pointing at the surgery, she said, "That man was shot at 4 o'clock in the morning and it's now 1 P.M. and if he lives it'll be pure accident."

"I wasn't aware that sort of thing was happening," the general said.

"Well somebody ought to be aware of it," Barbara snapped back. Suddenly she looked at him more closely. She didn't know one rank from another but something in his bearing made her suspect that he was perhaps more than an ordinary field soldier. But of course she had already plunged in too deeply for a meek retreat. "Do you have any—uh—influence with the troops in this area?" she said.

"A little," replied their commander-in-chief, not smiling.

"Well maybe you could get them to—I mean . . ."

"I will see what can be done." The general strode back to his car, where his driver and an aide snapped to rigid attention until he was seated. Watching, Barbara said weakly, "I have a sick feeling that I just spoke out of turn."

She hadn't. This became apparent next day when two ARVN trucks and an ambulance pulled up with a full load of shot-up soldiers, militiamen and civilians. Dr. Castellanos was still sorting them out when a Vietnamese army surgeon and his two aides drove up to announce that they were there to help and would stay as long as the emergency lasted. Just behind them came a huge tent to house the hospital overflow, and a truckload of surgical equipment.

"What made it all absolutely perfect," Barbara now says, "is that the wounded militiaman, the little guy who started the whole thing, didn't die after all, so it turned out we'd done each other a really good turn."

James K. Luce, graduate of the Yale medical school, class of 1952, interned in air force hospitals in Japan and India. Along with the practical aspects of medicine, he learned something about the benighted primitives of the world—that they are almost always open and warm to outsiders in their midst until given reason to be otherwise; that they need none of the trappings of Western civilization to be happy, only health and a little food; that only 15 miles from the modern city of New Delhi there was no medical care for them, none at all. He came out of the service to practice in Hawaii and California, took a year of surgery and began a three-year residency in internal medicine in Iowa City. And all the time he sought some way in which he could return to the Far East to work among its sick and destitute people.

In the summer of 1960, he read an article about Tom Dooley's work and wrote a letter to MEDICO expressing an interest in joining him. It was enthusiastically received and eventually arrangements were made for Luce to take over at Quang Ngai when Carl Wiedermann's two-year tour of duty there ended the following summer. This would give Luce time to complete the last ten months of his residency.

But Dooley had other ideas. Pressed by the dark shadow of death, he was pushing hard in these months to fulfill his commitments and to implant firmly in Southeast Asia the spirit and reality of MEDICO. In October, Luce had a telephone call asking him to join a team bound for Malaya (now Malaysia)—immediately. Against the advice of his professors and fellow residents, he agreed, and has never regretted it.

Before they left, Dooley explained MEDICO's mission. It was not, he said, to go into underdeveloped areas and set up sweeping programs of detection and elimination of diseases. They could not go to Malaya as public health agents because they hadn't the staff or facilities for the job. Nor were they going as teachers, prepared to make doctors out of native boys and skilled nurses out of village girls. Except for what they might be able to teach the local people who worked alongside them, they would have time for just one function: to give medical care where it was needed, to treat the sick.

The new team went to work in a government hospital in an area of rubber plantations and thick jungle. Malaria had recently been controlled—but not conquered—by a chemical spraying program sponsored by the World Health Organization. But malaria was quickly replaced as a tropical scourge by tuberculosis, which crippled long before it killed and disabled whole families, though only one member was sick. For then the others had to work longer and harder to earn the meager sustenance of life, and worn down, exhausted, endlessly exposed to the virulent bacilli, they inevitably fell victim to the disease themselves.

Fighting it with every resource available to him, Luce heard for the first time an astonishing criticism of MEDICO and other health organizations like it. In cutting disease in the underdeveloped nations of Asia, the polemic went, Dooley and the rest were contributing to a population explosion that would soon lead to mass starvation, since there could never be enough food to feed the increased millions. Says Luce: "The people who hold those views almost never get out of Singapore or Bangkok or Vientiane. If they did, they'd see a world full of half-sick men and women who are perfectly able to *re*produce but not to *pro*duce. And the thing is that there is plenty of undeveloped land in Southeast Asia to support a larger population, if only the people were well enough and strong enough to utilize it."

Once the program in Malaya was functioning, Luce was transferred to the hospital in Kratie, Cambodia, developed by Dr. Emmanuel Voulgaropoulos, and from there, in July, 1961, to Quang Ngai. "I came with qualms," he says, "for Carl Wiedermann had left a legacy in Vietnam second only to Tom Dooley's itself."

But of course neither Dooley nor Wiedermann had been able to do more than make a minute start against the immense tide of sickness and ignorance that overwhelmed the land. The problem of malnutrition persisted and plagued every doctor in every Dooley installation, although fruit and vegetables were easily grown and the rivers full of fish. Late one morning a stunted little boy, no more than twelve, came alone to the clinic at Quang Ngai, a rope basket clutched in both hands. Through the interpreter, Luce asked, "How can I help you? Do you have *dow bung*—pain in the belly?"

"I am not sick," the boy said softly. "It is my sister who is sick."

"Why didn't she come?"

"It is a long way. She is too weak to walk."

Luce sighed glumly. "I don't know how I can help her then," he said.

"Last time you gave her the powder that comes in the can. It made her well."

Luce realized at once that he was referring to Sustagen, a high-protein food supplement that produces good results in cases of malnutrition. He gave the boy another can, whereupon he reached into his basket and produced two ducks and three chicken eggs for the *Bac sy my*.

Luce closed his eyes for a moment against what suddenly seemed the monumental hopelessness of it all. Then
he patiently told the interpreter to say to the boy that if
his mother only added the eggs and poultry to the sick
girl's unchanging diet of white rice, and gave her also
fruit and fish, she would be healthy and no one in the
family would have to make this long trip to the clinic. But
he well knew that the boy's instructions would not permit
him to take the Sustagen unless his gift was accepted, so he
took the eggs and the ducks with somber thanks and
wished his distant patient a speedy recovery.

Except for weekend village clinics, Luce spent all his
time at the hospital, leaving execution of the immunization program to Barbara and Marcella O'Connor. It was
at the hospital that he could see the most patients, and at
the hospital, too, where the endless anxieties of logistics
came to focus.

Despite Chaney's best efforts, supplies remained a nagging problem. One shipment of drugs was irretrievably
ruined—and hundreds of dollars wasted—because some
poorly packed bottles of hydrogen peroxide broke and
contaminated everything else. They continued to scrounge
medicine wherever they could and the U.S. Special Forces,
who visited regularly, were especially helpful with stocks
of chloromycetin which they badly needed for their steady
run of typhoid patients. The irony was that some flourishing black market made it readily available in the towns,
even in Quang Ngai, and it could be bought openly without prescription by anyone with the cash to pay for it,
something Luce rarely had.

Improvisation kept them going. They learned to hammer shelves and tables and to do their own plumbing. And as for wells and cesspools, they could dig one between dinner and dark and never lose the thread of their conversation. "We were up to twenty-one cesspools when I left," Luce says, "and that must be a world's record for a bunch of people who had just found out which end of the shovel goes into the ground."

Though they were not equipped to launch a public health program, it was clear that some minimal instruction in sanitation might produce great gains, for the most frequently seen diseases of all resulted from polluted wells and indiscriminate toilet habits. Typhoid fever, hookworm, amoebic dysentery, all major problems, might have been prevented easily with only some rudimentary hygiene, but continued to run rampant. Hookworm was the commonest ill, affecting fully eight out of every ten children in their area, causing chronic bleeding in the gastrointestinal tract and often severe anemia. Then the wasted little patients had to be built up with iron before the hookworm parasites could even be attacked. "And all because they were constantly barefoot and went to stool wherever they happened to be when the urge came on them," Luce says.

He made a special effort to explain the connection between dirt and disease to the people who came to the clinic. In the villages, Barbara and Marcella would urge the women to boil drinking water and wash their hands before preparing a meal, and the men to dig good sound toilets. And they were grateful for every success, no matter how small, because successes were rare. Two cultures had come into conflict: the health measures the Dooley team advocated were alien, even frightening to the Vietnamese, and they would most often nod agreement and go on doing exactly what they had always done.

To dramatize the effectiveness of proper sanitation, USAID once designated a model village, sent teams in to build toilets and teach every family the importance of using them. Yes, yes, everyone said, they understood, and after intensive effort, the Americans were convinced that they had made a promising start and moved on to another village. But when they went back to resurvey their "model" a year later, they found that only the midwife and her family—5 people out of 220—were still using the toilets.

Among the American advisers to the Vietnamese 25th Division in the Quang Ngai area was an army captain named Harry Moore who, in various small ways, had been helpful to the Dooley hospital. There were those who teased Barbara that his interest was less humanitarian than personal, but the fact is that he was good-humored, quick with ideas—and his own labor—for their endless array of problems, and all hands were glad to see him turn into the compound. On one such occasion, when Harry stayed for dinner, Barbara grew increasingly restless as darkness came on with still no sign of the truck Marcella had taken south that morning on an immunization trip. Both girls had always made it a point to be back before dark, as much for the peace of mind of their interpreters and Vietnamese aides as because of actual danger from the Viet Cong.

Finally, at 8 o'clock, Barbara said, "Something's happened. I have to go look for her."

Harry raised troubled eyes from his tea: "But it's dark."

"Yes, well, that's why I have to go."

"Wait a minute. Take it easy. Let's—where was she bound this morning?"

"Duc Pho."

"Duc Pho! That's 50 kilometers from here."

"Forty."

"Okay, 40, but . . ." He stopped, then started again. "Listen, nobody owns this country at night. There are no government forces out and . . ."

"But Marcella's out. And, Harry, she wouldn't be unless something was wrong." She had gotten up and was already at the door.

"Well, wait a minute, damn it," he said following her across the room. "I'll go with you. I sure don't want to but I will. Where's your weapon?"

"What do I want with a weapon? I'm not going out to fight."

He sighed and they crossed the shadowy compound in silence. Barbara climbed behind the wheel of the ancient truck and they were soon clattering south on Route 1 toward the village of Duc Pho. The road thrust its way through the rice paddies, a white ribbon in the light of the moon, six feet high and barely two lanes wide. There were no crossroads, no side roads, no place to turn around, and the only sound in that brooding night was the anguished whine of the motor. Harry was hunched forward, peering hard beyond the bright fan made by the headlights, and when they had gone 30 kilometers or so, he suddenly commanded sharply, "Hold it! Stop! Cut the lights!"

By the time Barbara had brought the truck to a halt, he had vaulted out to the road, tense and still as he strained to identify the vehicle crouched darkly not 25 yards ahead of them. Then he leaned back in. "You take off without me if there's trouble, hear? I'm going to crawl over there and find out who that is."

"Okay," Barbara replied, "but try not to scare her too badly. It's Marcella."

"What!" He straightened up in surprise and cracked his head smartly against the door frame. "How do you know?" he whispered.

"I recognize the truck. Don't you?" She spoke in a normal tone, unable to resist teasing him a little more. "Anyway, here she is."

With that, Marcella strode up behind the bewildered officer, clapped him on the back—nearly causing him to leap to the top of the truck—and exclaimed, "Boy, am I glad to see you! There isn't one of us worth a darn at changing that flat tire."

Harry later reported that he didn't know whether to laugh or swear. He had gone at the expedition as though it were a desperate maneuver in small-unit infantry tactics—they were, after all, in a combat zone—and the matter-of-fact coolness of the two nurses, the way they had imperturbably taken him unawares, made him feel, all at once, idiotic. He cleared his throat and said, a little too loudly, "Yes, we were wondering what kept you," and heaved a silent sigh of relief because Barbara didn't laugh.

When he had changed the tire, they had to go another 15 kilometers before they came to a village where they could turn around. Not until they finally saw the lights of the hospital did he lean back in the seat. He even began to whistle. Then he asked Barbara to marry him. He said sheepishly, "I figure it's the only way I can keep you from telling the whole world about how I was playing John Wayne out there and you two outflanked me." Barbara stopped the truck and kissed him, and it was agreed that they would be married when her MEDICO service was finished.

The immunization program was completed in March, 1963. According to the teams' meticulously kept records, in little more than nine months they had given 195,450 injections to some 90,000 children in hundreds of villages and towns from one end of Quang Ngai to the other, including, they are certain, a good many controlled by the Viet Cong. "But what difference does that make?" Marcella once said. "A five-year-old child is not pro-government or anti-government, no matter what his father is. He's just a five-year-old child."

They traveled by truck, jeep, boat, helicopter and on foot, and except for the outermost three, reached every district in the province. They went into the mountains to immunize the children of Montagnard tribesmen, and to offshore islands whose people had no way of getting to the mainland.

Before long the Dooley hospital had no more diphtheria patients and only a handful with whooping cough. They had broken the cycle of reinfection and even without further immunization ensured a striking reduction in these diseases for years to come. As for tetanus, the results were not immediately so dramatic since they had immunized only children. But the future would see heartening gains here, too.

Meanwhile, the day-in, day-out tasks of the hospital

continued and the scope of its work broadened. They had set up a small training school for rural midwives, a new pharmacy, and a modern hospital kitchen, and a helicopter pad was hacked out of the brush so emergency cases could be brought directly in. The medical ward was greatly expanded and more Vietnamese were hired to help with the heavier patient load.

These new aides were particularly proud of the hospital and of the part they played in its operation although, again, the culture gap between East and West tapped the deepest reserves of patience on both sides. The Vietnamese, for example, were inveterate hoarders: they had had so little in their lives that they clung to every new possession in the face of all logic. One nurse, instructed to give each child who came to the clinic a handful of vitamin pills, still had nearly a full supply a month later. Why? "I give each child only one. I save," she explained proudly. And it broke Barbara's heart to have to tell her that one vitamin pill was about as useful as one wheel on a truck.

The entire concept of sterilization was foreign to them. Talking to the Vietnamese nurses through an interpreter, Marcella would insistently tell them that if they didn't boil an instrument for twenty minutes it was not sterile; that if they boiled it for twenty minutes and then used their fingers to pick it up it was still not sterile. They had to use a sterile instrument to pick it up. Did they understand? Yes. Were there any questions? No. So it was particularly disheartening for her an hour later to come upon one of the girls blithely sticking the pincer end of a pair of forceps into boiling water and removing it after only a minute or two.

It was at this point that the Vietnamese needed their full quota of patience, too. Marcella O'Connor was a bespectacled, no-nonsense professional who used to believe that once she'd carefully explained something the aides ought to be able to understand it. When they didn't, she voiced her displeasure in succinct, unsparing phrases, and if they failed to fully understand Marcella's sometimes uniquely American terminology, there could be no mistaking her tone. So it was that the sterilization episode called down on the hapless Vietnamese girl a ten-minute discourse on the responsibilities of a nurse, the importance of paying strict attention and the dangers of medical error. When it was over the girl apologized, then timidly said, "I am, of course, stupid. But a germ is so tiny—I have never even seen one—that I find it hard to realize and remember how it can make the people sick. Perhaps if you could explain it to us again. . . ."

Marcella did, gladly.

The close-knit team of Americans at Quang Ngai began separating early in 1963. Marcella, who was replaced by a gentle, good-humored Irish nurse and midwife named Rosaline Devlon, took up her long-postponed plan to cross India and Africa on her way home. "For a long time," Dr. Luce said recently, "the last I'd heard was that she had started across the Sahara Desert in a truck. And apparently she made it because not long ago I had a letter from USAID saying she'd given my name as a reference on an application for a nursing post. So she's surely back in harness somewhere in Asia."

As for Jim Luce himself, he had quite a trip home, too. Replaced by Dr. Patrick Reardon, an energetic Virginian, Luce drove a Land Rover from Vietnam to Ban

Houei Sai in Laos, where nurse Penny Watson and corpsman Reggie Gordon had been the only skilled medical hands at the Dooley hospital for weeks, and where there had been no regular doctor since the death of Carl Wiedermann. He stayed ten days, treating patients and greatly lifting the spirits of Penny and Reggie. Then he returned to the States to embark on a long program of cancer study and research, and to continue a close association with the Dooley Foundation, even pinch-hitting as acting director when Verne Chaney is visiting installations in Asia.

Before the Quang Ngai team members began going their separate ways, the Vietnamese hospital staff had a party for them, drafting in painstaking English a description of their feelings about each of the departing Americans. Of Marcella, they wrote:

"We never forget tall lady with eyeglasses of an extra observer who has the courage to express her dissatisfaction at any place. Please, Miss Marcella, receive our recognition and gratitude."

And of Luce: "There is a gentleman reserved, speaking little but working very hard. Some people would think he has no worldly relation but we found him in his heart and spirit full of charity and humanity."

Asked if he would go back when his cancer research is finished, it is hardly surprising to hear Jim Luce reply, "Any time I had the chance."

In April, 1963, Barbara Boyd went to Saigon. Her parents were living there, her father working on a comprehensive water system for the city and, as always, caught up by the urgent needs of its people, their numbers now swollen by refugees and their eternally desperate plight made even more desperate by the crisis of war. Barbara's agreed term of service was over, but for five months more she taught English to Vietnamese children at the Armed Forces school and went regularly to work at Madame Ngai's An Lac orphanage. Then she and Harry Moore were married and when civilian dependents were ordered out of Saigon she went to live in Bangkok. Although she has no official connection with the Dooley Foundation, she continues to do all sorts of odd jobs for them. She and Harry now have two children but she continues to hope that when his army service is over they will be able to join the Peace Corps.

"There's so much to do in so many places I've never even heard of," she muses. "If I can make a few children smile in some of those places, I'll get as much out of it as they will. Like that Montagnard kid . . ."

During the immunization program, she had flown by helicopter to a Montagnard village in the mountains. Among the last of the children to be inoculated was a bony little boy of three or four with a dirty piece of adhesive tape over a grossly distended abdomen. He wore not a single stitch of clothing. She was about to pull off the adhesive to have a look when the child's mother caught her hand and spoke to the interpreter.

"She say boy fall on sharp piece bamboo. She say"—he swallowed, then went on—"insides hang out."

Barbara took a deep breath. When she looked at the boy he returned her gaze with steady brown eyes, but not a flicker of expression touched his face. "Ask his mother if she'll let me take him back to the hospital at Quang Ngai. When he's better we'll send him back next time the helicopter comes here."

The mother looked quickly at the boy, then stared off at the mountains. Then she nodded abruptly.

When it was time to leave, nearly everyone in the village pressed as close to the helicopter as they dared, the little boy's mother and father in the very front. And though he stood in the open door watching them as long as he could—Barbara holding onto his thin arms from behind—no trace of feeling crossed his face.

As soon as they got to the hospital, José Castellanos had a close look at the jagged hole and protruding intestine and, next morning, repaired the damage in a simple surgical procedure. But without it, the boy would almost surely have died.

He never cried, either in the ominously gleaming surgery or afterward, when the anesthetic wore off, and he must have had considerable postoperative pain. Nor did he cry of homesickness or boredom through the long days of recuperation. But neither did that inscrutably blank look ever leave his face. The Vietnamese nurses tried to baby him but he seemed to draw back into himself, and since no one at the hospital knew the Montagnard dialect the gulf between them and the child was complete.

When he was better, Barbara took him into Quang Ngai town and bought him a pair of shoes, some trousers and a green sweatshirt that said, "Cornell, Class of 1975." It was the smallest one she could find, but hung halfway to the boy's knees. Then she bought him a little toy xylophone which he clasped in both hands, and though she showed him how to play it, he only held it tightly to him, now and then stealing a quick look at it.

It was clear he'd never worn clothes before and had several accidents before he learned how to get his pants on and off. But he became part of the hospital scene, the stern-faced tyke in the drooping sweatshirt who carried a silent xylophone wherever he went. Often Barbara took him to nearby villages in the jeep, and he loved to stand in the front seat, the wind full on him and whipping his fine black hair. But he never spoke and he never smiled.

When Barbara had word that a helicopter would be going back to the boy's village, she felt a tug of regret. And when the big beating craft came and she hustled him up into it she wished again that she could make some small contact with him. But there was nothing, just those brown eyes fixed on her as she backed away.

And then suddenly there *was* something—a look of panic, a wild questing of his face and his hands and his whole body, and the airman hanging onto him in the open doorway of the chopper cried out, "What is it? What's the matter?" Of course Barbara couldn't hear above the rotor's roar, but it didn't matter, for the boy didn't answer. He only looked her full in the face—and then made a graceful little movement with his right hand, as she had shown him how to do with the xylophone mallet the day she'd bought it for him.

And then she knew. She broke and ran for the hospital ward where, in the excitement of departure they'd forgotten the toy xylophone, and she found it at the foot of his bed and snatched it up, then ran back to the poised helicopter. He still stood in the doorway, eyes riveted on her and she ran up and thrust the xylophone into his hand. Then he broke into a full smile, and he waved at her, and he kept waving and smiling radiantly until the great roaring machine had lifted so high that she could no longer see him. And never in her life had she felt such a surge of happiness.

CHAPTER IV

Ban Houei Sai

IT WAS NEARLY a month after Jim Luce finally left Ban Houei Sai bound home before another doctor took off from California to replace him. Surgeon Stephen Thorngate landed in Bangkok on a hot and humid February day in 1963, a little bewildered by his first Southeast Asian metropolis and completely baffled about what he ought to do next. He needn't have worried. As he wrote to his wife a few days later, "Miss Watson, about whom I'd heard so much in San Francisco, came looking for me, took me by the hand and led me through every procedural problem between Bangkok and Ban Houei Sai."

Miss Watson, who was named Zola and called Penny, was a pert, slender nurse in her early thirties when she first went to work at Houei Sai in 1962. Since then, doctors and corpsmen had come and gone but she remained the Dooley Foundation's thread of continuity in Laos, the effective administrative head of the hospital and an incredibly efficient nurse. She believed in Tom Dooley's dream and worked for it with every last wisp of energy she could muster.

"For a long time," she says, "what we were running amounted to no more than an elaborate first aid station. But when a man brings us his child who's just been trampled by a water buffalo, he doesn't ask if we've been certified by the Alameda County Medical Society. The big thing is to be here, not like a tourist, but as part of what's happening to these people every day. Do you know I've spent the better part of the last five years in this part of the world and have never seen Angkor Wat or the Taj Mahal?"

She has seen much, though, of the world's poverty-plagued millions and the endless ills that fasten on them. A graduate of the John Hopkins school of nursing, she has served in international medicine since 1956 when she went to work at the Albert Schweitzer Memorial Hospital in Haiti. Returning to the United States to take her degree, she chanced to hear a talk by Tom Dooley and, afterwards, went to the podium to have a word with him. It was a momentary meeting, their only one, for Dooley had already undergone his massive cancer surgery, but it redirected her life. She told him she was a nurse and wanted to work for MEDICO in Asia.

"Go to New York," he said with no hesitation. "Tell them at headquarters that I sent you. And I'll see you in Cambodia or Laos before long."

He never did. Although he was able to make one last trip to the Orient, Penny was sent back to Haiti by MEDICO and not until October, 1962, when Dooley had been dead for nearly two years, did she finally head west across the Pacific. By that time she had fulfilled an 18-month commitment to MEDICO, left when it was absorbed by CARE and went to San Francisco to serve four months as a volunteer in the office of the hopeful young

Thomas A. Dooley Foundation. "In all that time," she remembers, "there was only one thing on my mind: a hospital in Southeast Asia."

The one to which she finally came, Ban Houei Sai, had had no regular doctor since the death of Carl Wiedermann. Reggie Gordon, who took over when Al Harris left later that summer, did valiantly just to cope with the steady press of patients and hadn't even time to give thought to anything else.

Penny was no novice. She took one look and knew that hard as she'd anticipated the job to be, it was going to be harder still. The hospital, built by Dooley, was now officially owned by the Royal Lao government and commissioned to TADF, which had pledged to provide personnel and equipment. Its mission, as set out in a formal agreement with the Minister of Health, was to meet the medical needs of the community and train local people eventually to take over while the Foundation team moved on to other needful areas.

"I thought this was an ambitious program," says Penny in an epic of understatement, "to be housed in a wooden building on stilts without plumbing and accommodating thirty patients in fifteen beds. But I'd come to work, not argue."

And work she did. With the fall of Nam Tha, Houei Sai had been established as the temporary capital of Houa Kong province and battle casualties drifted in from all directions. It was the unlikeliest seat of government, a ragged run of bamboo huts propped this way and that on a single dirt road paralleling the Mekong, women pounding rice below and two families or more squeezed into each single room above.

There was then no scheduled air service into Houei

Sai. Critically ill patients were evacuated by chartered plane—at TADF expense—or military aircraft if one was in the vicinity. And even that had to be done in full daylight, for nowhere in Laos, not even in Vientiane, was there a lighted landing strip.

But there was only infrequent need for such emergency measures. For most of the patients, ill with the common, chronic ailments of the underfed, unwashed and overworked—tuberculosis, malaria, typhoid, dysentery—there was little more that could be done anywhere than was already being done at the TADF hospital in Houei Sai. Initiated to suffering though she was, Penny was shaken by the breadth and especially the duration of the peoples' diseases. Most had been sick, not for weeks, but for months and years, nearly all the children bloated with worms and their parents so inured to pain that only crisis brought them to the hospital. Penny recalls one man whose dysentery must have persisted for years until, finally cured by medication and free of pain for the first time in memory, he returned to the hospital in panic to demand to know what sort of spell the *Bac sy* had cast over him.

The only medicine in all that part of Indochina was provided by TADF and—except for the fetishist ministrations of witch doctors—by the handful of native aides trained by Dooley or in one of his hospitals. This led to an awkward complication when uncounted Thais from across the river, with no medical help of their own, began bringing their aches and ills to Houei Sai. The Dooley team, though well aware of what this cost them in time and medicine, could hardly be expected to run an immigration station, checking each patient to be sure he was Lao, not Thai.

"Anyway," says Penny, "you can't say to a sick Thai,

'Look, we're under contract to the Lao government. You'll have to take your typhoid somewhere else.' There just wasn't anywhere else."

Nor could they run their river clinic down the Mekong and stop only at the villages on the east side. To governments and their officials, the international line of demarcation was very plain indeed. But to the people who lived on the river's two banks it was all rather obscure. They were ethnically the same, subsisted on the same marginal rice economy, crossed freely along the unguarded borders, and carried the same persistent diseases back and forth.

In the end, TADF's policy of necessity produced unexpected gains. Inevitably the pride of the Thai government was stung by reports of these wholesale medical migrations and they issued a no-nonsense order to the few doctors and *médecin chefs* in the northern part of their country to beef up their services and get out to the hinterland where they were so conspicuously needed. The flood of patients from the west bank of the Mekong slowed to a trickle and TADF, with clear conscience, could maintain their preeminent principle of asking the sick and the injured only where it hurt, not where they came from.

The river clinics grew in importance. Obviously the leaky longboat and its dogged outboard could carry Penny or Reggie to people without strength or means to make it to Houei Sai. But it gave them a chance, too, to bring something more than medicine to the villages. "If a Lao woman comes to the hospital," says Penny, "and you tell her disease is caused by dirt, she won't know what you're talking about. Give her a bar of soap and show her how to wash and it still doesn't mean much to her: it's just something people do in the hospital. But you take that bar of soap to her village—to her house!—and scrub her kid's grimy hands clean with it and you have a chance to reach her. She may even come looking for more soap when the first bar is gone. And it's the same with boiling drinking water, cooking the trichinosis out of meat and digging a decent toilet. I don't say they'll all do it. But you do have that chance."

A weighty question of protocol arose out of Penny's sex. As director of the Dooley hospital, she was automatically invited to the town's important social and official functions, and it was imperative that she attend. This was hardly a problem for her since she was honored to be asked and greatly enjoyed her meetings with the people. The problem was that such functions in Laos were traditionally and strictly for men only. And so, in one of those inscrutably Oriental ways, with not an overt word spoken, there was soon worked out an understanding that preserved the amenities without really trespassing on the common law: Penny would be invited to every ceremonious gathering; she would accept, blithely making the rounds of the reception line as though she were not the only female present, and even stay for an extra moment or two to avoid the look of a hasty departure. But ten minutes after her entrance, a silent alarm would go off in her head and she would turn to her host with profuse apology and explain that a seriously ill patient required her presence at the hospital. There would follow anguished pleas that she remain, loud cluckings of regret, and then she would leave—precisely on schedule—so the party could begin.

There were other customs she was to learn about during those early days, and among the most harrowing was the strange power of the *phi*, the spirits of danger and death

*Tom Dooley and Mme. Vu Thi Ngai with the
children at An Lac Orphanage, Saigon*

Verne Chaney with the late Albert Schweitzer

Dooley Foundation nurse injecting a young patient

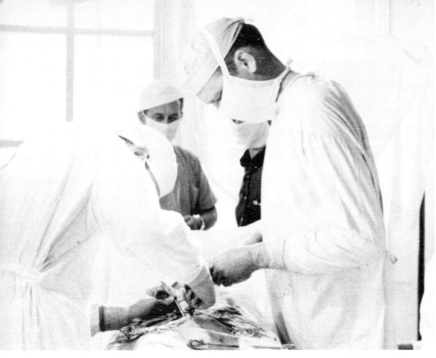

*Verne Chaney
doing surgery
in Cambodia, 1961*

*Carl Wiedermann with
two young friends
at Quang Ngai*

Dooley stewardesses with charges (above) in

Peter Purdy supervising work in Tibetan Handicraft Training Center

right) in Nepal

Tibetan refugees

Mrs. Susan Purdy teaching Tibetan refugee children at Mussoorie

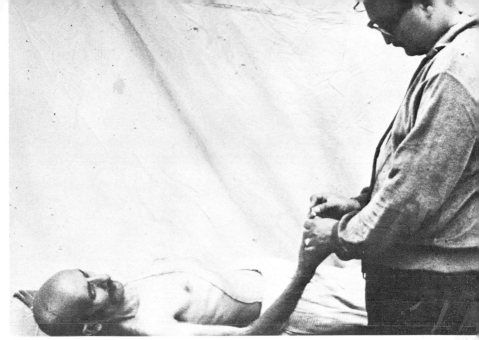

Dr. N. K. Shah examines patient in Nepal Health Survey

Technician Rene Allen taking chest x-ray during showboat visit to village

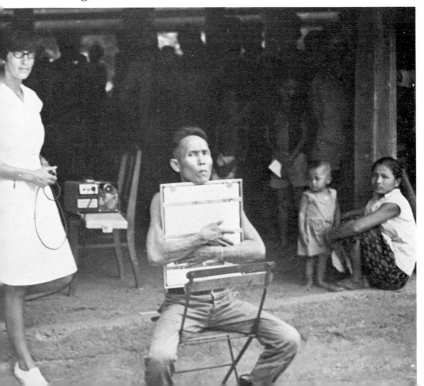

Showboat City of San Francisco *on the Mekong River*

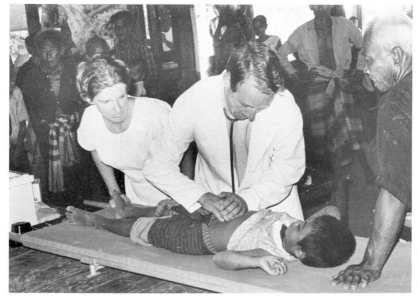

Dooley doctor examining young Lao patient on showboat

that could visit their evil on a man, a family—even a whole hospital. A runner brought word early one evening that there was a pregnant woman in great difficulty out on the Nam Tha road. Since military security along that road remained a sometime thing, Penny asked the Lao commandant to send a soldier out with Reggie and two aides. They came clattering back in the old jeep at about 8 P.M., the patient, a tribeswoman well past forty, softly crying with pain. Not long after, her family trotted after her into the hospital compound, squatting silently outside in the light from the ward, their faces troubled and expectant.

Penny questioned the woman through an interpreter: this was her ninth pregnancy, though she only had four living children; up in the mountains she had been in birth throes for four days when suddenly she'd had a single severe pain and labor stopped completely. That had been three days before. She had been trying to reach Houei Sai since.

An examination confirmed that the baby was dead. Penny gave the woman a mild sedative and went off to arrange for a plane to fly her out to Vientiane for the necessary surgery to remove the fetus. All through the night, at two-hour intervals, she returned to the ward to check on the patient, but her condition remained the same. Then, at 6:30 A.M., the Lao aide on duty tapped on the door to the staff quarters and nervously announced that the woman was dead.

Penny dressed and went at once to talk to the family. But the family was gone. And even as she watched, the other patients—including a few she didn't think could get out of bed—were gathering their few belongings and hurrying off into the thin morning light.

"Wait! Where are you going? What's the matter?" she called after them. Not one even stopped to answer. She turned on the Lao attendants: "What's wrong? Where is everyone going?"

But all they said was that things were bad, very bad, and then they, too, hurried off. In the space of a few minutes, only she and the corpse were left in the deserted ward and she was overtaken by terrible apprehension: were all their hard work and hopes to be undone by some blind superstition she couldn't ever get to the bottom of? What was she supposed to do? *Why had everyone left?*

"Okay, Miss Watson," she lectured herself aloud, "time for big girls to pull themselves together."

She went to wake Reggie and Tim Ford, a new corpsman who had arrived a few weeks before. When she'd briefed them on what had happened, they removed the body from the ward and Penny went again to confront the Lao aides. "You must help me," she said earnestly. "Tell me what's the matter. Don't be afraid."

They were not *afraid* to tell her; they were ashamed. Working at the hospital, in an atmosphere of reason and real things, they knew they should not be panicked by specters. But the practices of a lifetime were not easily shaken off, not in the face of such dire provocation. So finally they revealed to Penny that there was no more ominous omen among their people than to be anywhere near a pregnant woman who has died without being delivered of her child. When that happened the *phi*—the demons of evil, unseen but all-powerful—came in their full fury and struck out wantonly and maliciously, blinding, maiming, killing anyone luckless enough to cross their invisible path.

Penny took a deep breath. She realized at once that the time for debate and rational persuasion was later. Right now the immediate threat had to be countered. "The thing I had to do first," she has said, "was to get rid of those damned *phi* before my hospital got such a bad name in the boondocks that no one ever came back."

She went directly to Reggie and Tim and told them to remove the fetus from the dead body—though there are few more unpleasant surgical procedures than a post-mortem Cesarean section—and prepare both for separate burial. Then, moving as though the *phi* were after *her,* too, she drove into town to consult with the village elders, explaining what she had done and pleading for their help. And finally they set out to find the dead woman's family for her, then began elaborate preparations to exorcise the evil spirits.

The frightened relatives were tracked down in the late afternoon, whereupon the bodies were decently and promptly interred in separate graves. Immediately after, a wary file of old sages from Houei Sai and the villages around came chanting up to the hospital, moving with their incantations and liberal scatterings of rice through the ward, the lab. and surgery. When they had finished, they marched off in the same slow-moving ceremonial line, leaving word with Penny that the rice was not to be swept up: it was an offering to the gods whom they had beseeched to come and drive off the *phi.*

Two patients came back the next morning, four the morning after, and by the end of a week everything seemed back to normal. But Penny, who at this point wasn't at all sure that she didn't believe in the *phi* herself, wouldn't let the last of the rice be swept from the corners and crannies for a full month.

Dr. Thorngate stayed at Houei Sai from February to June, 1963, and was at work every waking hour. All the really complex cases on whom Penny had been able to delay treatment until the arrival of a doctor were now produced for the young surgeon, who was suddenly seeing more patients in a day than usually came to his office in Pebble Beach, California, in a month.

And such cases! A local man came in with a potato-sized tumor on his foot. "Dr. Dooley himself cut on this four years ago," he told the interpreter proudly. Not a week later there was a young woman with a severe knife wound, self-inflicted, in the upper abdomen: she had been trying to relieve her body of the *phi*. A seventy-year-old Chinese who'd had pneumonia was given an injection of some sort by his son. No one knew what it was, or even if it was injectable, since drugs of all sorts were sold promiscuously in the town. In any event, when the old man was brought to the hospital, he not only still had his pneumonia, but severe hepatitis as well, and a running abscess on the right buttock, where the hypodermic had been inserted.

These, the overwhelmingly *common* diseases of the people, and the grinding day-in, day-out battle against the fatalism of the centuries kept Thorngate—and all the staff —absorbed until he fell wearily into bed each night. And he learned, as had his more enlightened predecessors, that in the unending battle against ignorance, tact and a little guile were often the most telling weapons. Long before, Dooley was first to understand the unhappy dilemma in which these people were caught, tugged one way by his modern medicine, and quite another by the sorcerers and witch doctors who had long dominated their lives. And his straight-faced strategy, whenever he could use it, was to treat the local medicine men as fellow physicians. "The deal was," he once said, "that they could invoke the proper spirits if I could administer penicillin."

Six years later the strategy was still working. A twelve-year-old came to the hospital with a badly burned back, now raw and peppered with infected black blisters. The witch doctors had been treating it with cow dung and monkey blood, the father said. Thorngate was able to heal the infections, but just as he was about to start skin grafts the father announced that the spirits were summoning the boy back to his village. By now Thorngate had learned the futility of arguing and instead told the father that between the witch doctor's medicine and the *Bac sy's* the boy could be made completely well. But he must be returned to the hospital as soon as the spirits permitted it. Sure enough, in less than two weeks father and son were back, the boy's bandages untouched, and the skin grafts were a complete success.

Unhappily, neither the best strategy nor the best medicine could always overtake the spirits. Once a woman brought her two-year-old son to the hospital with yaws, his face a continuous sore and in places ulcerated through to the bone. She told Thorngate that the child had fallen sick only a few days before, although it was clear that the disease was months old. That case had obviously gone to the local witch doctor first, only now it was too late for Thorngate to do anything but clear up the worst of the lesions: the child's face would always be a grotesque mask.

Most disheartening of all were the instances in which relatives carried a patient away from the hospital because they became convinced that he was going to die, and that unless he died at home the spirits would not know where to find him, leaving his soul to wander forever in some awful purgatory. A winsome little boy with advanced carcinoma of the leg came one day, wasted and spindly, but so brave in the face of enormous pain the he crept into everyone's heart. Had the leg been promptly amputated, there was a good chance for him to live. But the family wouldn't hear of it. They said he was going to die, accepted some medicine for the pain and took the boy home—where their grim prediction inevitably came true. But with all the disappointments and poverty of equipment, no American could come to Houei Sai without sensing that TADF was doing something somehow deeply important. Writing home, Thorngate said, "Puny, insignificant organization that the Dooley Foundation is, with its ramshackle hospital probably not worth as much as a single air-conditioned room at the Embassy, I think that here perhaps a miniscule scratch is being made on the broad hard shell of Southeast Asia. Real patients are being seen and treated, not many out of all the millions, and maybe not too well by back-home standards. But it's a beginning. And we have the immeasurable advantages of Dooley's name and the most dedicated, hardest-working people ever to come out of the U.S.A."

Penny Watson once wrote to a friend that "If you make perfect plane connections and don't mind losing the sleep, Houei Sai is six days from San Francisco, two days from Bangkok—and about ten minutes from a fat ring of real estate held by the Pathet Lao." Yet when she left in September, 1963, to return to San Francisco for orientation and a new assignment, it was an emotional wrench.

There have been new TADF assignments for her ever since: Vientiane as administrative director; India to review medical facilities for Tibetan refugees; Nepal to lay the groundwork for one of the Foundation's most ambitious projects, a comprehensive health survey of that mountain-locked land. In 1965, she became overseas program director, taking temporary leave to study for a master's degree in tropical medicine before returning to active duty with the organization she says has given her more than she can ever hope to repay.

The first replacements to what was now the only TADF hospital in Laos—Canadian nurse Margaret Alberding and laboratory technician Barry Seeley—were soon followed in fairly regular succession by a corps of eminently qualified physicians. Among them was Dr. Robert F. Conway of San Mateo, California, who brought along his wife Margaret, a nurse, and paid both their air fares out of his own pocket—except for $40 in pennies, fervently saved by his daughter Maureen and contributed to help defray her parents' expenses. Dr. Richard Baldwin wanted to volunteer while in college, right after he'd read Tom Dooley's books. But Dooley urged him to finish his education first, which he did, and came to Houei Sai as soon as he'd completed his internship. And Dr. José Castellanos, the fine Dominican Republic surgeon who had already served at Quang Ngai, returned to TADF duty in Laos in February, 1965, and served two years more. Meanwhile, Chaney had worked out the details of the airline stewardess program—the first two went to Mussoorie, India, to work among the Tibetan refugees in 1961—and soon a procession of lovely, earnest young girls, each of whom had volunteered for Asian duty and been given a two-months' leave of absence, was brightening the ward at Houei Sai and in countless small ways reducing the workload of the medical staff.

None of the newcomers lost any time adjusting to the demands of life in a jungle hospital. No one could afford them that luxury. Each day brought its invariable load of new patients and old diseases, and each week brought at least one crisis.

The Conways hadn't even unpacked when they had their first. As they were walking down the road to pay their respects to the Chaokhoueng and the mayor, an agitated farmer came panting after them and said, through the interpreter, that his little boy had fallen in front of a water buffalo and been kicked "and now his eye is funny." Dr. Conway jumped into the jeep with the father and two Lao assistants and went speeding through the jarring ruts to "the third village on the Nam Tha road." There, on the dirt floor of a dark and airless little hut, lay the child, perhaps seven years old. His right eye was hanging out.

Conway carried him out to the jeep and they raced back to the hospital where ether was administered and the eye removed. Describing the episode to her own children in California, Mrs. Conway wrote, "The poor boy was so dirty and feverish that we all had a whack at him with soap and cool water. Major surgery is usually evacuated to Vientiane but in an emergency like this, the TADF hospital is it." She did not add that without it, the unlucky child would have died.

Not long after, Conway was making rounds in the ward when three lepers wearing a few filthy rags for clothing walked in. The oldest, with a ruined face and feeble step, looked at least seventy, the other two almost as weak and quivering with fear. As well they might: the other patients, still believing leprosy—or more properly, Hansen's disease—to be a spiritual curse and highly contagious, rose from their beds to swear at the miserable trio and throw things at them, and would have beaten them into bloody retreat had Conway not physically intervened. He separated the two groups and tried to calm the patients, assuring them that they had nothing to fear from the lepers. Still, in the end they all stood firm on their threat to leave unless the pariahs were banished at least as far as the hospital porch. There Conway and the nurses tried to make them comfortable. They had assumed that the three were grandfather, father, and son, but the truth was that the infirm and doddering "grandfather" was only forty years old and the other two were his sons, aged twenty and twelve. They had been afflicted a long time, and four years before had been driven from their village, doomed to go wandering across an increasingly hostile land since then.

Medically, there was little to be done for them: the disease had had too long a time to work its inevitable destruction on their bones and tissues. But Conway did clean and bandage their lesions and his wife gave them hot, nourishing food, then soap to wash with. "They scrubbed and scrubbed," she recalls. "They didn't really know why, but they wanted to please us—anything so they could stay a little longer." Stewardess Shirley Turner took some money a friend had sent her and bought them clothes in the town, burning their pathetic rags, and the expressions that crossed their faces when they saw each other in decent clothing—astonishment, gratefulness, a certain tentative return of pride—gave her, she says, all the reason she ever needed for her service in Laos. And when they left—as, of course, eventually they had to leave—she felt the full impact of Asia's tragedy.

One day only a bare handful of patients came to the clinic and some of those on the ward went home. When it happened again the next day, and the day following, the Americans were deeply worried that something had gone wrong. "The doctor was sure that we had somehow offended the people," Shirley says, "and I thought maybe the Pathet Lao were frightening them away." It was Pat, the translator, who, finally realizing his colleagues' concern, explained: it was rice-planting season; no one could take time to be sick.

Early in 1963, TADF's faltering, outboard-powered river boat was replaced by a sleek new jet-propelled craft painted in dazzling orange and decorated with pictures of the Walt Disney cartoon character, "Lady." Now the desultory village visits, heretofore limited by the old hulk's fitful state of repair, became a regularly scheduled floating clinic. When, soon after, a new orange jeep and trailer were delivered to Houei Sai for thrice-weekly medical trips up the Nam Tha road, a basic new dimension was added to the Foundation's work in northwestern Laos.

As Chaney wrote to the Houei Sai staff, he had not suddenly discovered a gold mine. But his persistent efforts to find and stir up Dooley supporters across the United States finally began to pay off with the establishment of Foundation chapters in half a dozen cities. It was the New York chapter that mustered the $4,500 for the 20-foot river boat—christened "Lady" by singer Peggy Lee, newly named chairman of the TADF board, on the second anniversary of Tom Dooley's death—and the Indianapolis group that produced funds for the jeep and trailer.

For the nervous, scrimping little band in San Francisco headquarters, this new support lightened the brooding dark cloud of impending financial disaster that had so long hung over them. And for the men and women they had sent off to Laos, the boat and jeep, gifts from people half a

world away, meant that medicine and hope and the deep-
felt concern of ordinary Americans could be brought to
additional thousands in the far-off villages of that dark
land. The highly visible orange became TADF's official
color, and the cartoon characters from the Disney world of
animated fantasy became the beginning of a common language between Asian and American.

Even with new equipment, neither the boat nor the
jeep trip in any way resembled a Sunday outing. The
coffee-toned, seemingly turgid Mekong swept dangerous
heaps of driftwood downstream and often the medical
team had to cling to the gunwales as Toomb, their nervy
pilot, wrenched the wheel this way and that to avoid
shoals and eddies. Depending on the season, the jeep con
tended with inches of mud or dust, and with jungle, rotting
bamboo bridges, and the proximity of the P.L. Past the
first 25 miles up the Nam Tha road leading to Muong
Sing and a few miles further on, into Red China, the ter-
ritory was "disputed." Before each trip, the staff had to
promise the Lao colonel responsible for their safety that
they wouldn't venture that far. Often, though, they did,
because as Penny Watson once put it, "People get just
as sick there as they do here."

And the sick ones came to the hut of the *naidang* or village chief—where the visiting Dooley team usually set up
—as many as 200 of them, removed their sandals and sat
patiently on the floor waiting for their turn, meanwhile
listening to each other's symptoms and nodding sagely,
though not understanding a word, to the *Bac sy*'s diagnosis
and prescription. Most could be treated with vitamins,
antibiotic ointment, chloroquine for malaria and aspirin
for *jip ayo*, or aching back, especially prevalent because of
endless hours spent stooped over in the rice paddies. All

the seriously ill patients were brought back to the hospital.

It soon got so that nothing surprised the TADF staff. Driving back one early evening, they rounded a bend and almost knocked over a Yao tribal lady running up the road, both arms waving them to a stop. Her teeth were stained black with betel nut and her dark hair worn hanging to the waist so the good spirits would have something to hang onto when they came to pull her to heaven. Talking briskly to the interpreter, she first apologized for being too late to catch them at the village clinic: she lived far away and had been walking all day. Then she announced that she was pregnant and wanted an abortion because the *phi* had taken hold of her and she was certain her baby would be born blind or dead.

Bob Conway considered this with serious mien. Then he said that unluckily he hadn't brought along anything for an abortion. But he did have some medicine that would drive off the *phi,* and rummaging in his bag, he produced a bottle of pills and handed them over with instructions to take one a day as long as they lasted. She thanked him lavishly and marched back down the road, happily regarding her prize. It was a bottle, almost full, of a Vitamin B complex, particularly beneficial for pregnant women.

Once Dr. Castellanos led a team to Ban Dahn, some 20 miles upriver—where his first patient was an elephant. A village elder, waiting for them at the dock, anxiously explained that the elephant, which hauled logs from the jungle, had a sore on its underside; if it felt too ill to carry on, the sawmill would have to shut down and many of the villagers would be thrown out of work. Warily Castellanos went to look, and his staff held a collective breath as he hunched down under the elephant and peered up at its vast expanse of belly. He came out to tell the interpreter that the "sore" was an abscess which should be dressed with an antibiotic ointment. It took eight tubes.

The Dooley people took home a conglomerate of memories and a kaleidoscope of sights and sounds: the way every Asian child seemed to have a younger one strapped on; the color and sweet smell of the frangipani trees; the woeful reluctance with which patients confessed to a toothache—with no dentist, there could only be one treatment at Houei Sai: out! Dr. Conway remembers civilization rearing its fateful head: though there were perhaps ten vehicles in all Chieng Khong, the Thai town across the river, he had two auto accidents victims in one day. They didn't tax the other drivers with negligence or threaten to sue. They simply blamed the *phi* and let it go at that.

Lao logic was always disarming. The people—most of whom had never seen a refrigerator, stove or bathtub—spoke blithely of taking a plane to visit relatives in Vientiane or Luang Prabang. They would make the long walk out to the airstrip where there was no shelter nor even any shade and sit on the ground in the hot sun hoping a plane would land that day, and that it was going where they wanted to go and that the pilot had room for them.

Juanita Tiffany once described herself as a navy brat who became an air force nurse but didn't really find out what nursing was all about until she went to Southeast Asia. Between her father's military service and her own, she had lived in many of the world's far places and, having volunteered to go to work for TADF, was unawed when Verne Chaney said he was going to send her to Laos. "He told me it would be rough and I kept saying, 'Fine, fine— that's what I want.' "

She went to the library and borrowed language records in Lao and French. She read all she could about the land and its beleaguered people. And still nothing prepared her for the stark reality of Ban Houei Sai. "I got there at the beginning of August, 1965," she recalls, "and probably didn't come out of shock until September."

She was shaken to find two or three patients sharing a bed, stunned that a man's whole family would stay right in the hospital with him until he was released. Then there were the wounded, always a substantial portion of the Houei Sai caseload—grown heavier as the intensity of the undeclared war picked up—and the near-certainty that the casualties who came in without family were Pathet Lao. It was a well-understood little charade in which no information was volunteered and no questions were asked. And less than a week after her arrival, she had her first death.

"I hadn't even seen a fatality since I got out of training," she says. "Military nursing isn't at all spectacular, you know—everyone is young and healthy and all you ever get are some flu's and an occasional appendicitis. Then on my second day at Houei Sai they brought in this soldier with a great gaping bullet hole in the chest and Dr. Castellanos was off on river clinic and he was all mine."

The man had been three days without medical help and was already moribund. Tiff went to work cleaning the wound—the bullet had driven right through the chest wall and back—and administering intravenous nourishment and drugs, then two small tubes to drain deadly fluids. The patient drifted in and out of coma and sometimes tried to speak but couldn't, though Tiff could read in his eyes that he understood she was trying to help him and was beholden. He was a small man with a sad face and he was very frightened. Tiff prayed aloud for the doctor's return. But when Castellanos came there was little more to be done. They could have used oxygen to help the wounded soldier breathe but they didn't have it, and a larger drainage tube, but they didn't have that either. So they did the best they could and, indeed, for two days he seemed to be getting better. But on the third day the very effort to draw breath into his tortured chest undid him and with a last rattling gasp he died even as Tiff was trying to raise him to an easier position and clinging to him as though she could help him cling to life.

She was badly upset, but only for the rest of the day. For early next morning, four more seriously wounded patients were brought in and there was simply no time to brood.

That was a Wednesday. On Thursday three helicopter flights brought in seventeen fresh casualties and José Castellanos operated well into the night, Tiff and Nurse Sheila Weygman by his side. One man with a bullet hole through the stomach required a major bowel resection and while Dr. Castellanos cut away several feet of intestines, Tiff pulled out a five-foot tapeworm. But the patient needed considerable blood and when, toward morning, they ran out, he died, too.

Working almost around the clock, turning from patients who were lost to those who could be helped, Tiff had no time to wonder, let alone ask, why American helicopters were bringing Lao war wounded from places where there wasn't supposed to be any war. It was just as well, for these were questions to which only a few knew explicit answers, and they weren't saying. "After you'd been there a while," she remembers, "you sort of absorbed the truth: that if the war in Laos wasn't as big as the one in Vietnam it was just as tough, with the same sides and the same stakes."

In the last days of 1965, it came to Houei Sai. On December 28, a TADF truck delivering medicines to a village dispensary 32 kilometers from the hospital was ambushed by the Pathet Lao. The driver tumbled out and hid in the brush long enough to see the P.L. assassinate the *naidang* and drive off with the vehicle. Then he made it back to Houei Sai through the woods and reported, and Dr. Castellanos put all hands on P.L. alert: they slept in their clothes and had drugs and equipment packed and patients ready for immediate evacuation. Suddenly the little town was overrun with Royal Lao soldiers, their trucks churning great dust clouds and their mortars emplaced behind every fold of ground.

Next day there was shooting and someone brought word that 600 P.L. were bound up the Nam Tha road toward Houei Sai. The people panicked. They plunged down the hill to the river and pleaded and thrust their way aboard anything that floated and appeared to have even a remote chance to make it across the Mekong to Chieng Khong. The Lao hospital personnel stayed only until the doctor told them they could leave if they wanted to, then they, too, crossed over to Thailand and only Castellanos, Tiff, and Sheila Weygman were left with the patients.

There were new rumors every hour. But the small arms fire which grew steadily louder was clear enough, and so were the planes that flew over the tangled undergrowth on strafing and bombing sorties. An American military adviser to the Royal Lao army drove up on the thirty-first and urged them to evacuate, but Castellanos said he could not go anywhere unless provision was made for his patients. The young officer then looked at the two nurses. They said nothing but stood motionless alongside the doctor and the officer shrugged and went away.

Just before 7 the next evening, New Year's Day, there seemed to be a lull in the firing and Tiff went down to the ward to distribute some Christmas candy to the patients. With no warning the earth out front was torn apart and flung skyward and the awful cr-rump of a mortar round exploding rattled the walls and deafened them. And as the sick and wounded Lao huddled terrified in their beds and Tiff ran to blow the kerosene lamps out, eight more rounds crashed into the hospital compound and shattered windows and engulfed them all in stunning noise and the hot, corrosive smell of gunpowder. Every patient who could move fled from his bed and through the door.

"Wait!" Tiff cried out. "Where are you going? You have no place to go!"

And running to stop them, to reason with them, she knocked over a kerosene lamp and at once flame rolled out across the dry wood floor. She spun back to try stamping it out and on the periphery of her vision saw a patient, an elderly woman with her leg in a cast, fall heavily as she tried to get down the hospital steps and lie still on the darkening ground. "It was all like some wild west movie," Tiff now says, "only there was nobody around to make sure we had a happy ending."

Except she herself. When the fire took hold of the floor and began creeping up one wall, she snatched up a blanket and, flailing this way and that, finally beat it out. Then she ran to the steps and coaxed the woman in the cast to her feet and half-led, half-dragged her back inside. There were two other nonambulatory patients left, a man in a body cast unable to move a muscle, and a four-year-old girl suffering convulsions who seemed to have passed out with fright. And there Tiff sat in the dark with them, not certain of anything except that she couldn't leave them, regularly murmuring in Lao what few words of comfort she could think of, while grinding trucks and the irate shouts of soldiers turned the road up the hill to turmoil.

In a little while, Sheila crept down from the staff quarters to stay with her. Dr. Castellanos had gone for help, she reported. Soon after 9 P.M., he returned with two missionaries and a jeep and in two trips they got the immobile patients down to the river. It was decided that Tiff would take them across to Thailand while the others remained behind in case the other patients came back and to protect the hospital from looters.

It was the crossing that Tiff most dreaded. She had heard the hair-raising stories of the evacuation in 1962 when Carl Wiedermann and Al Harris made it over but scores of others had drowned in the frenzy of overloaded boats and skittish helmsmen. What would she do about her three helpless charges if their boat tipped?

As it turned out, she never had time to worry about that. After a long wait on the cold, creaky dock, she and her little group were finally loaded aboard an already crowded longboat—whereupon the child went into a convulsive fit from which it did not seem she could come out alive. Tiff had no tongue depressor so she jammed her comb in the girl's mouth to keep her from biting her tongue off, and she held her close and prayed for the nightmarish journey to end. When it did, past midnight, a Thai official standing on the darkened riverbank said the foreigners had no permission to land and would have to stay where they were until he had further orders.

Tiff sat quietly for a few moments, the little girl shivering in her arms. Then she got up, still carrying the child, and managed somehow to climb the steep, slippery bank. The official ordered her back. "Do you speak English?" she asked.

He drew himself tall. "Yes," he said.

"Then I want you to understand that this child may die if I can't get her some medicine and a warm bed very soon. And I have two other patients in that boat—we're from the Dooley Foundation hospital—and I not only want to land them immediately, I want you to find us some transportation to take us to your hospital. Can you do that for us?"

"Yes, ma'am," the man said solemnly. And again, "Yes, ma'am!"

Twenty minutes later Tiff had her patients in beds in the dark and unfinished Chieng Khong hospital. Scrounging through the pharmacy, she found a few ampules of some sedative and a hypodermic syringe and was finally able to get the little girl to sleep. In the morning, red-eyed with weariness herself, she got someone to look after her improvised ward and returned to Houei Sai for food and medicine.

Sixteen patients and ten relatives had reappeared at the hospital, and these, too, Tiff led back to Chieng Khong. There she pushed her eight remaining beds into pairs, assigned four people to each, and invited the rest to join her on the floor. And in this way, crossing the river each morning to get food, inventing games to keep her charges diverted, laughing with them and allaying their fears, Tiff passed four tense and uncertain days. "For the first time

I understood something of what it meant to be a refugee," she says. On the fifth day, the fighting on the other
side of the Mekong ended and they went back. There had
only been fifty or sixty P.L. involved in the attack, Tiff
later learned, but at one point they were within 7 kilometers of Houei Sai.

And, as always, there were failures to temper the gratification at each success. A young woman, five months'
pregnant with her first child, began having premature
labor contractions and was on the verge of aborting when
she reached the hospital. They put her to bed and gave
her medication and in time the contractions stopped. At
the end of five days it appeared certain she would carry
her baby through to full term. But that evening, when Tiff
stopped on the ward to visit her, she was quietly crying
into her pillow.

"What's the matter?" Tiff asked.

"The *phi* came. I am going to lose my baby."

"No, no." Tiff cradled her and murmured, "You're all
well. You're going home tomorrow!"

She seemed comforted and eventually fell asleep. But at
4 A.M. the night nurse came rapping on the door of the staff
quarters and by the time Tiff reached the ward the girl
had aborted.

"It sounds weird and thoroughly unscientific, doesn't
it?" Tiff said recently. "But it's only the perfectly ac-
ceptable Western psychology of mind over matter with
Oriental trimmings. Haven't you known excellent American surgeons who refused to operate because the patient
was convinced he was going to die?"

In the end, the rigidly fixed ideas of the Lao people would have significant bearing on Tiff's TADF service. When the Foundation stepped up its efforts at the 200-bed government hospital in Pakse, a sleepy Mekong River town 500 air miles south of Houei Sai, Tiff was assigned there to assist in the operating room and teach the Lao nurses O.R. procedures.

At 5 P.M. one day, Dr. Alex del Carmen, the highly skilled surgeon from the Philippines who'd settled in Pakse and become a staunch friend of TADF, sent word that he needed her for an emergency operation: a farmer from Champassak had been gored by a water buffalo 30 hours previously, the wide-ranging intestinal wounds already infected and adhesions forming. It was difficult and dangerous surgery, with Tiff administering anesthesia and Dr. Alex excising more than five feet of intestine. But the man left the operating table in good condition and Tiff stayed by his side almost constantly until he was out of danger. In a week he was strong enough to eat solid foods and take a stroll on the veranda. In a few days he would have been ready to go home. But when Tiff came on duty the morning of the eighth day, he was dead.

"None of the night nurses knew why," she says. "He just died. But I found out why by taking one look at the table by his bed. Somebody had given him the wrong medicine."

She was shaken by the discovery, but only in that first stunning moment. She had been in Laos long enough to learn that medical aides—*médecin chefs*, nurses, corpsmen —got only enough training to start them off. There were neither teachers nor time to do more, for all over the land millions waited for whatever small relief could be sent. And so blunders like this were inevitable, and had to be weighed against the belated efforts of a nation just developing to help itself.

The episode led to an additional assignment for Tiff—and to disaster. She persuaded the hospital director to let her conduct a daily class for the fifteen or so Lao nurses at the hospital, basic instruction in sterilizing techniques, pharmaceutics, patient care—"All the things I learned in my first year at nursing school." And she went eagerly from nurse to nurse explaining the program she planned and telling them to be sure to be in the dining room promptly at 9:30 A.M. But at 9:30 A.M. no one was in the dining room but Tiff.

Bewildered, hurt, she went back to the director. "It was a mistake," he assured her. "They didn't understand."

So again she went from one to the other. "Please be there tomorrow," she said. "You will learn a lot." And they nodded and said Yes, yes, they would be there. But next day it was the same and at last Tiff knew it was no mistake.

"These were no village girls willing to have you show them how to apply a Band-Aid," she has since said. "Some of them had had 15 years' nursing experience and although they may not have known how to use an autoclave or mix a prescription they were human enough not to want some hotshot American sticking it in their craw."

And so Tiff learned the hardest lesson of all, how patience and tact could be swallowed up in the timeless ways of Asians, and totally lost to the infinite importance of face. But she knew, too, that the only worthwile resources of Westerners were more patience, more tact.

"Of course I had to quit," she says. "I had lost face and no Lao would take me seriously any more. But that didn't matter much. The work went on. Others would be along to do the job and once I was gone the things I tried to do would again be possible."

The work went on for Juanita Tiffany, too. Even while she was still in Pakse that summer of 1966, wondering what to do next, a U.S. government agency asked if she would be interested in taking up nursing duties at a remote and highly secret American base. So the chances are very good that she is still somewhere in Southeast Asia, still dreaming Tom Dooley's dream.

CHAPTER V

Khong Island

ON KHONG ISLAND at the southernmost tip of Laos, in the early evening, one can often hear in the distance the rolling thunder that seems to promise a summer storm. It is not thunder. It is the sound of high explosives, bombs and artillery shells in endless tons, tearing apart the secret trails that parallel the Cambodian border a few miles away and lead to the back door of South Vietnam. No one at Khong knows where the aircraft and the big guns come from, only that their constant interdiction of communist infiltration routes brings the Vietnam war quite close indeed. Then, if the radio is out and no plane has been able to get in for some days—there is a road to Pakse but it has long been held by the Pathet Lao—an American in the village of Muong Khong is apt to feel very much alone, and perhaps even to wonder if anyone in San Francisco or Vientiane, or even in Pakse, remembers that he is there. And at the edge of this village, 100 yards from the point where the Mekong broadens and then slices between the high hills of Cambodia, the Dooley Foundation has for five years maintained a small hospital and extended its audacious assault on the ravages of back country disease to the 10,000 people on the island and the 50,000 more in Sithandone province. Chaney made preliminary arrangements with the Minister of Health to provide staff and assistance at Khong in 1963. By the end of that year Tim Ford and Vorapat Patipatanakoon, the multi-skilled Thai interpreter known to all hands as Pat, had flown down from Houei Sai to survey the situation and begin integrating TADF's effort with the small Lao hospital, then staffed by an *infirmier indochinois*—a male nurse whose medical proficiency was considered to be a step down from that of a *médecin chef* —and a few partly trained Lao girls. In January, Canadian nurse Margaret Alberding joined them, and a month later Khong's first doctor, David Stanley, who brought his wife and two blond and blue-eyed young sons.

Islanders and newcomers regarded each other with mutual astonishment. Except for a handful of French colonials many years before, the people of Khong had never seen any Westerners and their curiosity was boundless—and uninhibited. Reports Dr. Stanley: "Imagine having eight or ten people squatting by your children's bed when you tuck them in at night, following you into the john to watch you brush your teeth. It was a month before I could come home and not find all the chairs occupied by a parade of smiling strangers."

As for the members of the Dooley team, none had ever seen either so primitive a medical facility or so lush and lovely a setting. Khong Island, set in mid-Mekong, is perhaps 12 miles long and 6 wide, and ablaze with rampant tropical growth—hibiscus, gardenias, mangoes, bananas, coconut palms and pineapples. A jeep-wide road runs along the river and joins most of the fifteen villages, each one an unworldly collection of thatched huts propped on stilts and surrounded by sun-warmed rice paddies. On both sides, the river is dotted with innumerable smaller islands. Directly to the south looms the deep green Cambodian shore.

The hospital was a long low building whose equipment seemed to consist of a few tables and chairs, a pole with an enema can suspended from it and an unsavory little charcoal pot for boiling the entire supply of syringes—two. The Americans took to calling it a 30-mat hospital as beds were in woefully short supply. There was no electricity and every drop of water had to be carried up from the river. Since there were no staff quarters, Dr. Stanley and the others had to rent houses from the villagers. "Ours had mud walls and a leaky roof," he recalls, "and a big old pig and her family living under the kitchen." When Nancy Stanley got down on her knees to scrub the floor, her Lao neighbors were so entranced by the sight they ran to bring others to watch.

Some months before the Stanleys came, the Health Minister had assigned a *médecin chef* to Khong. He finally arrived at the end of February, a nervous young man named Theo Phouphan who went from fits of friendliness to something between indifference and hostility, which he then tried to cloak by stalking off somewhere to take a nap. More and more the Dooley people counted on the *infirmier*, Theo Chi, a native of Khong with an unquenchable thirst for medical knowledge and motivation enough to keep him working long after everyone else had gone to sleep. His salary was 13,000 *kip* a month, about $26.

And more and more David Stanley—and the Dooley doctors to follow him—came to count on Marge Alberding, the slender, soft-spoken nurse who had already served ten months in Houei Sai. No newcomer to boondocks medicine, Marge had spent much of her nursing career working among the Eskimos and Indians in Canada's desolate northlands. And stirred by Dooley's death in 1961, she began a two-year letter-writing campaign to persuade, first MEDICO, then Chaney, that she had something useful to contribute to the work in Southeast Asia, and that her interest was real.

From the beginning, her primary concern was to temper the frightful mortality rates among pregnant women and their newborn. Tramping through Sithandone province, reaching outlying villages by boat and motorbike, she completed a survey whose conclusions confirmed the grim statistics she had first confronted in Houei Sai: that one baby in two dies before it is four months old, and that most of these fall victim to malnutrition, dysentery, tetanus and infection, every one an ill that could be warded off with only a little knowledge. "Look at what happens," Marge Alberding has said. "When a baby is born the cord is cut with a sharp piece of bamboo. And when the mother is too weak to provide nourishment, as often happens, the infant is supplemented with rice and Mekong riverwater. Then it usually becomes sick, death following in about a week."

She kept thinking about organizing a comprehensive midwife training and maternity program, possibly with help from UNICEF and the World Health Organization. But before she could make a beginning, when she had been in Khong only a few months, all the TADF team was suddenly face to face with a more urgent problem: cholera!

It began with some vague rumors from Cambodia. And then the terrifying reality was on them—feverish, dehydrated patients with agonizing intestinal pain, the first deaths and dark dread in the villages. How many were affected? How much vaccine did they need? How many immunization teams? Having radioed for emergency supplies and leaving Phouphan in charge at the hospital—where there was virtually no medication useful against cholera—Stanley, Marge, Chi and the Lao aides set out across the province to assess the spread and intensity of the disease. They walked miles from one village to the next asking their baleful questions—How many were sick? How many had already died?—and pleading with the people not to give in to their panic and flee. "Wherever you go, you risk spreading the sickness without protecting yourselves. Stay here and we will send medicine!"

When they returned to Muong Khong and compared findings—at least one or two deaths in each village, another sad cluster of people sick and isolated—they knew that all the potentials were there for a raging epidemic that would decimate the province. By radio and telegram they pressed for massive and immediate help from the Minister of Health, USAID, and their own headquarters in Vientiane. Then they began to count the hours.

Late that afternoon, a village *naidang* was brought to the hospital in coma. His people hung back nervously as Dr. Stanley performed the examination, but it was clear they meant to stay and find out whether the *Bac sy* had any powers at all against the terrifying killer disease. And the thing was that at the moment Dr. Stanley hadn't much. He administered some glucose injectable, but the sick chief never stirred from his clammy stupor, and his blood pressure kept dropping ominously.

"We've got to get some fluids into him," Stanley muttered, as though to himself, then suddenly turning to Marge, said, "Listen, sterilize a small glass with some whisky and mix me up some baking soda, salt and sugar with boiling water. And hurry!"

When this emergency potion was ready, Stanley fed it into the *naidang*'s vein—and then they began counting minutes. For they knew full well that without proper medication, the odds were strong that the patient was going to die quite soon. And then his people, watching fretfully from just beyond the hospital door, would return to the village to tell how the American doctor could do nothing to help even a chief, and that desolate word would spread to the other villages, and almost surely all the people's fear would erupt in blind stampede as they scattered and ran from the scourge, they knew not where. And then whenever the vaccine arrived, it would be too late.

In little less than an hour, the shock of the improvised injection forced the *naidang* back to consciousness. His eyes came drearily open and he tried to say something, and even as Marge bent close to wipe his forehead with a cool cloth, the sound of an airplane buzzing the hospital electrified them all with fresh hope. The little silver Helio Courier had flown in from Vientiane with the first of the emergency medicines.

The chief and three other critically ill cholera patients on the ward were soon out of danger. But the real work, the massive effort to direct the vaccine across the province and immunize 50,000 people in the shortest possible time, was just begun. Luckily neither the Health Ministry nor USAID stinted. Until darkness, and again the next morning, aircraft of every description swooped down on the lumpy Khong landing strip and unloaded hastily organized immunization teams and vaccine and syringes by the case lot, then flew back for more.

It was the sometimes ignored *infirmier*, Theo Chi, who pulled the wide-ranging plan together. Huddling over a large map of the province with every team that came in, he sent each one to a particular area, starting first with the hardest hit, showed them how to get there, and then somehow scared up the necessary transportation—jeep, motor scooter, boat, anything. Nor was that the end of it for this remarkable man. Once all teams were in the field, carrying enough supplies for at least three days, he himself set out for the villages, going wherever panic threatened to transform a quiet settlement into an unreasoning mob, calming the people and assuring them that the worst of the danger was passed.

Day by day the immunization teams returned limp with exhaustion, and still Chi pushed on. No one knew when— or if—he ate or slept, or how many miles he covered on foot and over water, but he did not rest until every man, woman and child in the province had been immunized. And when he came back, it was to report to the hospital, as always, for the 7 A.M. clinic. But David Stanley would not let it pass so easily. He took the brown hand of his Lao colleague and shook it very hard, and he said, "I want to tell you something. I want to say that I am very proud to be associated with you, *Doctor Chi.*"

Pakse, 70 miles up the Mekong, is Khong's link with the outside world. Water buffalo amble along its paved streets and lounge in the front yards. But Pakse, a town of 25,000, has a 200-bed hospital, the only X-ray equipment in southern Laos—a gift from the Dooley Foundation—and, in Alex del Carmen, one of only six fully qualified medical doctors in the entire country.

Born and educated in the Philippines, Dr. Alex took his postgraduate training in the United States and, after a surgical residency in Manila, went to Laos as an Operation Brotherhood volunteer in 1958. Tom Dooley became his close friend and ever since, TADF teams from Khong to Houei Sai have good reason to be grateful to this generous and good-humored man who came to understand Laos, its protocol and its sources of power, and who has shared his knowledge and friendship with the Foundation.

For Dooley newcomers to a land so different from their own, Alex del Carmen is an unfailing source of guidance, confidence and hard, practical advice. When young Jack Hjelt replaced Al Harris as area administrator in March, 1966, it was Dr. Alex who led him to a garage used as a TADF warehouse and showed him a pile of ancient electrocardiographs, sphygmomanometers and diathermy machines. With the best of intentions, they had been donated by retiring doctors in the States—and were less than useless. A bare handful of people in all Laos knew how to use them and they were meant, moreover, to measure and treat ills that came low on the list of the country's prevalent diseases. And so they sat, moldering.

"Tell them to send you some stainless steel basins and a good microscope," Dr. del Carmen gently told the new man. "Aspirin, vaccines, vitamin pills—you can do practically everything here with only the basic equipment and the basic drugs."

Jack Hjelt had a lot to learn and he had to learn it quickly. Before he left the states, Chaney told him what little he could about the job, that it involved administration of a loosely organized and far-flung organization, bill-paying when there were no funds, constant improvisation because nearly all problems were new ones, morale-boosting for all TADF hands in Laos, and complaining for all shortcomings to headquarters in San Francisco. And with that much to guide them, Jack, age twenty-seven, his wife Chris, and their daughter Traci, age three, flew halfway around the world to Vientiane to take up largely unknown duties.

They promptly lost track of each other. Flying between Houei Sai, Khong and Pakse, Jack wasn't home five days in the first five weeks. Even after his hectic period of orientation was over he remained gone more than half the time, for the Foundation's administrative problems in Laos were always intricate, usually urgent and seemingly endless. Then there was the uncertain matter of air transportation, provided by USAID on a "space available" basis, and the even more random lines of communication.

"Late," says Chris "used to mean an hour or two. Here it's a question of days, and all you're left with are thoughts of malfunctioning airplane engines over all that Pathet Lao country."

Once Jack went to Pakse "for a day or two" and couldn't get back for a week. That time she *really* worried and—after the gladness of reunion—Chris remarked testily that he could have sent a telegram. It seems that he had. It was delivered the *following* week.

Luckily Chris's hours were crowded, too, and she didn't often have time to brood. The Dooley house, a larger one than the Harrises had occupied, on the same street and marked by a Moorish entrance arch, became a sort of Grand Hotel, with new volunteers bringing new crises—a lost suitcase, an overlooked inoculation, and always and invariably their intestinal havoc. Somehow, though, Chris made time to give English lessons to the girls in the government training school, and to teach herself the Lao language. Soon she was interpreting for Jack, who never found twenty consecutive minutes for anything but the immediate problems of TADF. Even more important, Chris's mastery of a little basic Lao endowed her with special respect in the eyes of the people. And there were tangible results: her American neighbor, wife of an Air America pilot, might pay 200 *kip* for a few mangoes, but Chris, who knew the words and ways of the morning market, paid 30 *kip* for the same mangoes—and came away with the grudging admiration of the Lao vendor.

There would be times when circumstances forced Jack himself into lending a medical hand, though except for watching the TADF doctors in action, he had no medical training whatever. One night in Houei Sai, when José Castellanos was away, a pregnant woman in severe pain was brought to the hospital and Si, the Lao corpsman, could detect no fetal heartbeat. He asked Jack's help— which consisted of agreement that they had a dangerous situation on their hands unless they could somehow force delivery of the dead baby. After repeated radio attempts failed to raise Vientiane, Jack, who spent most of his airborne hours studying a pharmacopoeia, remembered that dextrose in solution had been known to induce labor.

"For all I really knew about it," he has said, "the stuff could have killed her. But the pain she was in, I think she'd have appreciated that."

As it happened, it did no such thing, but instead precipitated delivery of the dead infant exactly as it was supposed to do. The woman hemorrhaged in the process, but between them Jack and Si were able to control the bleeding, and by 1 A.M., they had her cleaned up and sedated and fell wearily into bed themselves.

The new area administrator had plenty of nonmedical problems to keep him awake nights. "I look like a clean-cut American type, don't I?" he once told an interviewer, then hunched close and with mock ferocity added, "The truth is, I'm an operator, a wheeler-dealer, an international con artist."

"Wasn't that Tom Dooley's technique, too?" he was asked.

"I never knew him. But it stands to reason, doesn't it? You're the Dooley Foundation, right, and you've got no money and no influence—except with a gang of Laotians in the back country who have even less. But still you have to pry a consignment of supplies out of some Thai shipping agents; you want to keep from being swallowed up by a high-pressure American aid mission; you try to get a Chaokhoueng to help you set up dispensaries in a few villages. What have you got to work with except a little skullduggery?"

But Jack Hjelt was nearing the end of his physical resources. He had never really shaken the persistent dysentery that was his introduction to Asia and in the summer he lay abed for nearly a week with dengue fever. Around Christmastime he took Chris and Traci down to Khong— it was the first time since their arrival that either had left Vientiane—but while there he suddenly lost consciousness and it was a full day before Dr. Mary Davia could bring him around. She deduced that he had a particularly acute virus infection again and careful treatment soon had him up and out of bed. But it was clear that his resistance was all but gone, hardly surprising in light of the fact that in the past months he had lost 50 pounds from his normal

160. In February, Chaney assured him that a capable replacement was en route—it was to be Earl Rhine who, nine years before, had established the hospital at Muong Sing with Tom Dooley—and at the end of March, 1967, Jack Hjelt and his family left Asia. No one who knew him there doubts that he will be back.

Children in Laos are not named until they are a year old because so many die in infancy and the parents believe it better that they return to the heavens unknown. It was the wretched plight of these children that got to Marge Alberding. For all the sickness and suffering she had seen in ten years of nursing, she could not dispassionately accept the dismal truth that all the earliest days of all these tots were a struggle just to stay alive, their little bellies bloated with intestinal parasites, soft dark eyes rarely ever free of pain. And these were the "healthy" ones. The sick ones sometimes vomited worms, and their blood sank to such a dangerously low level that it was hard to know how life could be sustained. She ached for the mothers and fathers who came to the hospital to sit by the beds of their little ones all through the long night, whose eyes begged the doctor to help when there was no help, and who, in the end, wrapped frail bodies in a blanket and took them home to die.

And one day the tragedy of the Lao children reached right into the heart of the Canadian nurse. A lovely little girl named Baysee lived next door to her in Muong Khong and they became fast friends. Baysee loved to sing and came often to Marge's room with a new song she had invented and stayed to look at the American magazines and, all seriousness, to correct her grown-up friend's persistent efforts with the Lao language. Once, when Marge badly burned her leg in a sterilizing accident, Baysee brought her sweet cakes and fruit and sat in the corner of her bed all day, ready to run errands, talk or just quietly be there for company. Thereafter she came with some small gift for the nurse every evening and Marge began to teach her English.

One day Baysee became ill. It was during the period when Dr. Stanley had left but before Dr. Davia arrived and the child's worried mother took her to Phouphan, the *médecin chef*. He found only that Baysee had some mysterious and virulent infection racking her body with fever, and that none of the medicines on hand helped at all. Marge spent hours sponging her friend's wasting little body with alcohol in an attempt to force her temperature down. But almost as soon as she was finished, it flared again to dangerous heights.

At the end of a week, Baysee lapsed into coma and Phouphan said her case was hopeless. But Marge sent an urgent message to Alex del Carmen in Pakse imploring him to fly to Khong to see if there was anything he could do for the child. She suggested that he bring some injectable broad spectrum antibiotics. And then she sat in her own room praying the long hours by, unable to sleep in dread anticipation of the wailing cries from next door that would signal the end of Baysee's unequal battle. But there was only the sound of a howling dog, and at daybreak the raucous awakening of the roosters.

Just after 9 A.M., Dr. Alex flew in with the antibiotics. Together he and Marge worked over the nearly exhausted child, and Marge continued alone when he had to go back, and by the following morning the intensive treatment and the drugs had brought Baysee back to feeble consciousness. But the obscure malady had a relentless grip on her—already there were signs of irreversible damage to her brain and eyesight—and before long the fever raged again and now Marge didn't know what else to do. The next night, as she was preparing her evening meal, there tore through the soft dusk between the two shadowed houses an anguished outcry. She started to run toward it, then stopped, realizing that there was no longer any hurry. She would let the family have their first moments of grief alone. Later she would take over some food for them.

After the burial, Marge sat in the gloom one evening and fingered the little gifts she had collected for Baysee during the days when there was hope that she might still enjoy them. Suddenly she sensed someone else in the room and spun around: standing inside the open doorway was Baysee's older sister, Khomphiou, a hesitant nine-year-old, with a sweet cake in one small hand, a ripe banana in the other.

"For me?" Marge said in Lao, forcing back tears.

"Yes, for you. I bring them now as Baysee used to?"

"Yes, yes." She held out her arms and the child ran into them, and as they clung together Marge let the tears come. And later she gave Khomphiou the little gifts she had saved and said, "Shall I teach you some English words?"

It was around that time that Marge submitted to TADF headquarters a formal proposal to initiate a rural midwife training program at Khong. When the World Health Organization and UNICEF agreed to help with supplies and teaching aids, the program was approved and preparations made to begin classes on November 1, 1964.

The first school building and maternal health clinic was an ancient shed of cow dung and mud donated by Phouphan. When someone leaned against a wall, it collapsed. When a carpenter arrived to repair it, he fell through the floor. But with the encouragement of the staff and Pat Patipatanakoon's untiring help, walls and floor were repaired, the outside whitewashed and the inside hung with sheets for sanitation and public health posters for instructive decor. When a real door was installed to keep out curious dogs and pigs, they were ready to open shop. On October 30, eight shyly smiling Lao girls, ages eighteen to twenty-one, from Sithandone and Attapeu, the neighboring province, arrived to present certificates attesting that they had completed six years of primary education. Classes began the next morning.

The first weeks were devoted to lectures and practical work. It was never easy, for Marge's command of Lao was still limited, and sometimes it was necessary for Pat, who stood loyally by, to translate so that the young midwives-to-be clearly understood their lessons in obstetrics, prenatal and infant care. Dr. Chi taught classes in hygiene and public health. And all difficulties were overcome by the students' very intense desire to learn. They took to coming back to the classroom for two or three hours each evening to sew baby clothes for the new mothers who would soon be their patients, and to discuss earnestly the lessons of the day. Marge encouraged this practice by bringing them little cakes she learned to bake in a kerosene can oven, and gradually won their complete confidence.

"It was necessary that they trust me completely," she has said, "because nearly everything I had to teach them was alien to what they had grown up to believe."

Lao women never prepared any sort of layette until

after their baby was born lest it bring bad luck. During pregnancy they ate only rice and salt, believing that other foods would poison the unborn child. And after confinement, the mother lay close to a hot fire for seven days, which often so weakened her that she fell victim to one of the host of diseases lurking in every village.

"And the thing is," says Marge, "you can't *force* anyone to change ways so deeply ingrained in them. So that becomes the hardest job of all—to forget for a while that you're a doctor or nurse or midwife who can order people to do this or that. They'll smile and say, 'Yes, yes,' because the Lao are so polite it makes you want to cry. But as soon as you leave they'll go back to the old ways."

What Marge taught her girls was to gain their patients' confidence by going along with those customs that did no particular harm, and by trying to moderate the worst effects of others on the basis of reason and understanding. Did the women insist on lying alongside that hot fire immediately after giving birth? Very well, "but tell them that if they move away from it on the second day they will feel stronger on the third." Was rice an invariable and unchanging part of a pregnancy diet? All right, "but make them understand that if they eat fruit and fish, too, their babies will be healthier."

Meanwhile Marge added regularly to the stock of basic requirements in the clinic by reminding UNICEF of her needs and drawing on TADF supplies whenever they were available. Little by little more furniture appeared, beds and dispensary equipment. The lying-in area was partitioned off with homemade curtains and stocks of vitamins, soap, and tinned milk were prepared for the kits the girls would eventually take into the field. But day by day another vital lesson was hammered home: that what they learned was infinitely more important than supplies or even drugs, for someday they would be on their own, without TADF or UNICEF, and they would have to make do with whatever was easily available in Laos—and what was in their own heads and hearts.

At the end of a month, the practical training was extended to include the care and teaching of real patients in the clinic. Recalls Marge: "That first group must have thought they were going to lose their skins from the no-nonsense way those girls washed them." Four weeks later, the fledgling midwives began going out to the villages, their own when they were close enough. And riding her motorbike from one to the other, Marge was never too far away to help with a difficult case or an unexpected problem.

There was a full quota of both. Once a student came looking for her anxiously to report that a patient, wife of a prominent police captain, was about to give birth—in a house full of old crones and witch doctors. Marge promptly went there, elbowed her way through the near-bedlam around the unfortunate woman in labor and sought out the chief witch doctor. She expressed pleasure at his interest in her patient. She said she was proud of the opportunity to work with him—if he had no objections—and when he grunted what she took to be an assent, she leaned in for the kill: didn't he think that the two of them could handle the case without his—here she paused meaningfully—assistants? He grunted again, shooed the coughing men and betel nut-chewing women out of the room and commenced his ceremonial chants and the tying of countless strings symbolizing the unborn child's ties to the gods.

Marge stood by nervously, but her strategy did not misfire. When it was clear that the baby was about to be born, the witch doctor gathered up his strings and, in the manner of a great surgeon ordering the resident to close up the incision, told Marge to carry on. Then he left.

Almost immediately her eight students came trooping into the room to see if all was well. They had gathered to lend her moral support but were afraid to come in as long as the witch doctor was there. Marge assured them that all was indeed well, and thereupon delivered a fine, lustily wailing boy to prove it!

Then there was a woman who lived on the edge of Muong Khong and who could not be induced to relax a frenetic daily pace despite the fact that not once in nine previous pregnancies had she carried to full term or delivered a live baby. And though even now there were clear warnings that her pregnancy might terminate prematurely, it was always Mrs. Khamphan who came running to the clinic—she never walked—with word of a complication or an imminent delivery in the village. The midwife-in-training who called on her found her most often chasing a chicken or hacking weeds in her small vegetable garden. Nothing could persuade her to rest, not even a huge bundle of sewing that Marge once brought to her in secret hope that she had found a way to keep her problem patient quiet for at least a week. Next evening Mrs. Khamphan ran all the way to the clinic with the bundle slung over her shoulder. Everything was finished, she told Marge with a bright smile.

To no one's great surprise, her baby, a girl, was born early in the seventh month of pregnancy, a crinkly faced mite of humanity weighing less than 4 pounds.

"She will die?" the new mother asked mournfully.

"She is very small," Marge replied. "But we will do all that can be done."

There was, of course, no such thing as an incubator in Laos, so she took the infant to her own room where she kept an improvised vaporizer going night and day to help her breathing. She fed her intravenously to supplement the driblets of milk she was able to take by mouth. And somehow the precious spark of life was preserved and the child survived. And thereafter Mrs. Khamphan brought her faithfully to the well-baby clinic each month—running all the way—and, waiting her turn, would tell the other mothers that she had finally given birth to a live baby because the nurses had been wise enough to make her rest during the pregnancy.

The training went on and slowly the eight novices were transformed from giggling teen-agers to serious and responsible young women. The clinic flourished, too. At first only women in great difficulty could be persuaded to come to them—Lao babies were traditionally born at home and childbirth was considered unexceptional despite the awesome mortality rate. But as the months passed and word spread that mothers who had had the clinic's prenatal care were delivering healthier babies—and that not one had died—more and more made their way to the little mud building in the TADF center as their time approached.

Soon it became clear that the building was not adequate. In June, when her students went to the maternity center in Pakse to complete their practical training and take their examinations, Marge packed a bag and flew off to San Francisco to see how best funds could be raised for construction of a new and permanent maternal health and child care clinic, and for the equipment needed to run it. There it was agreed to send appeal letters to past Dooley supporters—which Marge decided would have most impact if she wrote them by hand and mailed them from Khong Island. By the end of July they were on their way and although small donations began coming back almost at once, the really electrifying news arrived in a deceptively slender envelope in early autumn: a group of young children in Arlington, Massachusetts, wrote that they had heard about this latest TADF undertaking and that they had decided to "adopt" the midwife program as their personal project. Enclosed was a check for $2,000.

The spacious and completely screened new maternity center, with shower, bath, toilet and electricity, was completed the following summer. True to its promise, UNICEF then provided some 2 tons of equipment—clinic furnishings, jeep, boat motor and just about everything else Marge's little midwife group needed to function. Meanwhile, her first eight students, having completed their training and passed their examinations, bade her a tearful farewell and set out on the long journey back to their own villages where clinic subcenters had been set up for them. There, riding their UNICEF bicycles and carrying their midwivery kits, they would bring a measure of professional care to people who had had none, their own people, and so would light still another dark corner of the land.

Marge watched them climb into the truck that would start them off and her heart was full. She had come to look on them as younger sisters. She knew their weaknesses and problems and the intense conviction that had set them on this path. And now, beaming and proud in their neat new uniforms, they seemed so frail against the scope of all they would be expected to do. The four who were bound back to Attapeu, a province of 53,000, would represent the only medical attention those people would ever know.

And yet it was a beginning. Musing about the changes she herself had seen in her two years in Laos, Marge thought it not impossible that one of their sons might be a real doctor, one of their daughters a nurse.

As the truck rounded the corner of the compound and was lost in its own dust cloud, she waved a last goodbye and went back to the clinic she had envisioned in a day-dream, fashioned out of unremitting effort, and brought to life with persistent hope. There was a lot to be done. Her new class of aspiring midwives was coming soon.

When Dr. Mary Davia went to San Francisco to talk with Chaney about going to work for TADF in Asia, he warned her that the practice of medicine would often take second place to the other roles she would be called on to play.

"What?" she asked innocently.

"Father confessor to the staff, mother superior to the people and first sergeant to everybody."

"Oh no," she came back. "I'm just not that type."

Chaney smiled. "That's tough," he said.

And it was. Mary Davia, who calls herself a charter member of the live-and-let-live school, soon learned that for millions of people the business of staying alive in Laos was neither automatic nor guaranteed. To nurture and protect life against desperate poverty and inexorable diseases she found herself doing things she had never done before, thinking thoughts she had never had had, re-casting a set of values that came stamped, "Made in the U.S.A."

She had been born in Pittsburgh in 1918, served as an army nurse in New Guinea and the Philippines during

World War II, and found herself restless and somehow ill
at ease in postwar America. When her brother suggested
that she go back to school and pursue her medical skills,
she went to the west coast and pursued them so long and
so assiduously that in 1957 she emerged with a degree she
could hardly have anticipated ten years before when it all
began: Doctor of Medicine. She practiced in California
for a while but again the same restlessness overtook her.
Once she saw Tom Dooley on television and was deeply
impressed with what he was doing. When she read the
news of his death, she felt that short as it was, his life had
particular meaning and she wondered about her own.
And at last she telephoned TADF headquarters in San
Francisco, then went there to talk with Penny Watson
and Dr. Jim Luce who had served two years in Asia. When
Chaney asked how soon she would leave she said Now,
and a month later landed at Khong Island.

"There ought to be an intermediate step," she has since
said. "To come from the examining rooms and waiting
rooms and the meticulous hospitals I was familiar with to
a place like this is to be picked up and flung backward in
time. It calls for some getting used to."

For Mary Davia, M.D., it called not only for a change in
attitudes but in her very pace. She felt she had much to
give and she wanted to give it—right away!—and the seeming apathy of those to whom she brought her skills quickly
discouraged her. There was sickness everywhere and
everywhere a needless waste of life, consequence of those
twin harbingers of death, ignorance and superstition. And
yet when she set out assailing them with her medicines
and her knowledge, they slunk into the shadows before
her and reappeared at her back.

On one of her first river clinics, she came with an interpreter and a Lao aide to a village never before visited by a Dooley team. The people gathered at the *naidang*'s house and she thought she saw hope on their faces. She thought she saw it in the eyes of a young mother who stood suddenly before them, a small dirty bundle gathered up in her arms, though the woman offered nothing but her silent presence. Carefully Mary folded back the rags and saw that the bundle was a dying baby. It was perhaps six weeks old, its tiny body emaciated, dehydrated and gray with the ravages of prolonged diarrhea, principal killer of infants in the backwater villages.

Mary turned to Sam Chareonphan, the interpreter: "Tell her there is nothing I can do for the child here. We must take it back to the hospital. The mother can come, too."

But when Sam translated the message the woman turned her eyes on the people crowded close—none returned her look, none stirred—and then shook her head.

"She says No," Sam said.

"But why?"

"She will not say."

"Tell her that without help the baby must die."

They sought out the child's father standing watchful and still among his people and he too shook his head. They questioned the villagers with their eyes but were answered with blank stares. Each one remained motionless, passive, not one volunteering a word or sign of encouragement, not one raising a voice in behalf of the helpless infant who could raise no voice to save its own life. And so Mary examined the few people who would permit it, distributed some pills to those who would take them and then the disheartened Dooley team left—without the dying baby. And back in the boat Mary Davia changed from doctor to woman and cried bitterly at the senseless waste of life.

Later she would say, "I know in my heart that that mother hoped for something better. But she didn't dare take the first step. She had to conform to the ways of her people even if it cost her baby's life. And her people hadn't yet accepted us."

Nor had Mary yet accepted the Laotians. It took a long time before she realized that their apparent indifference and lethargy was really sickness, that nearly every one of them was malnourished even when they had enough to eat because of the worms and parasites infesting their bodies, their blood thin with anemia from repeated bouts of malaria. So many seemed content to squat in the sun and watch the world go by and at last Mary perceived that it was because they hadn't the strength to do much more.

And so she came at last to understand the Lao's submission to the supernatural. He knew no other way to explain the ills that haphazardly crippled him and killed his children, or the natural phenomena that sent the rampaging Mekong slashing through his village to destroy his home and carry off his pig. It had to be the evil spirits, the *phi,* and they became very real to him. They brought him misfortune and death and he resigned himself to death because no one had yet given him cause to hope for anything better.

"And finally I understood what Verne Chaney was talking about," Mary says. "That was my real job, more important than my actual medicines—to give the Lao a little hope."

But there were limits beyond which she would not indulge their fancies, and then she had to match her wits against their heedless dread. Once a woman came to the hospital with a goiter so huge she had to carry it in a sack.

The other patients were horrified: the woman was clearly possessed of the *phi,* they moaned in fear, and if she stayed they would all be afflicted.

"But she is sick," Mary said. "I cannot send her away."

"Then we will go."

"Wait until tomorrow. Surely the *phi* will not harm you in one night."

Next morning Alex del Carmen flew in for his twice-monthly round of surgery at Khong. In a simple thyroid operation he removed the woman's goiter and Mary took her back to the ward looking as normal as any of the others, with only a small bandage to mark the place where her horrendous growth had been.

"What happened?" the other patients asked in awe.

"There were too many of you for the *phi,*" Mary answered with only the trace of a smile. "They were afraid and ran away."

They saw through her little joke. Slowly they came to believe that the *Bac sy's* medicine was—sometimes—too powerful even for the *phi.* And so they took a first small step toward that shred of hope. And even as Mary began to reach them, their beliefs worked on her:

"All this *phi* business sounds primitive and silly, but how about we overdeveloped Westerners? We're beset with bigger fears than any Lao can conjure up and we don't even know what they are. A Lao can point to what bothers him, call it an evil spirit and try to avoid it. All we can do is take tranquilizers by the ton and run to psychiatrists and say is, 'I'm nervous. I'm insecure.' We'd be better off with a few *phi.*"

By river and land she traveled to the distant villages. And because she stayed and persisted and so plainly cared, the people thronged to the boat landing or surrounded the orange truck, the sick and the curious. And the time came when they led her into their dark little huts where the most desperately ill lay on mats, filthy and feverish and surrounded by the witch doctor's potions, and they asked for her help.

That spring a man brought his daughter to the hospital with a severe leg laceration. Mary stitched the wound and gave the child a tetanus shot and some antibiotic, whereupon the father began to dress her, ready to leave.

"But she must stay," Mary protested. "She can't walk."

"Then I will carry her," the father replied. "It is rice-planting time and I don't have time to remain here or come back for her."

But more and more they *were* coming to the hospital. Soon Mary instituted a system whereby mothers who agreed to leave their sick babies could stay or come back to feed them at mealtime. "Only they had to feed what we prepared. That way they found out that a child needs more than rice."

In time the hospital became one of Muong Khong's popular gathering places. The children came to play with the staff's collection of pets—a civet, a lemur, a monkey, two cats and a dog—and their parents stayed to watch the afternoon clinic. Once Mary had to perform a circumcision on a five-year-old boy and attracted such a crowd that she laid down a new rule: henceforth all surgery that couldn't wait for Dr. Alex—who was unmoved by an audience—would be done in the middle of the night.

Marge Alberding, a Catholic from Edmonton, Canada, and Pat Patipatanakoon, a Buddhist from Bangkok, Thailand, had been colleagues since their days at Ban Houei

Sai and close friends almost as long. At Khong a deeper and more meaningful relationship grew between them and in April, 1965, they were married in a Catholic ceremony in Vientiane. Early in 1967, Marge gave birth to a little girl and soon after the new family flew off to Canada, Pat to study engineering and Marge to continue nursing.

Mary Davia stayed on until the end of the year, when another doctor replaced her. Her most vivid memory of Khong is of a New Year's *baci* given in her honor. A *baci* is a Lao ceremony held on all important occasions, its high point the tying of strings on the wrists, each string carrying a good wish for the recipient. Mary's were already laden when still another woman squatted before her and began to go through the ritual. This is how Mary described what happened next:

"She said something I didn't understand—truthfully, I wasn't paying much attention—and I turned to Sam. He told me she'd said, 'Doctor, don't leave us. Stay and take care of our babies.'

"I think I grinned foolishly, but only so I wouldn't cry. All of a sudden the past two years had meaning and the year ahead promise—I could believe these people had accepted us. They were giving up death and defeat and beginning to hope."

She stayed on in Laos working for TADF and promoting its cause with all her strength. "Listen," she will say to visiting Americans, "do you know how lucky you are? To be born there? It's just an accident, you know. Do something with it! Don't just sit there and be fat and comfortable. Remember that except for some quirk of fate you could have been one of these faceless Asians."

CHAPTER VI

What Can One Person Do?

"ONE DAY WE WENT out to a place where 300 refugees were arriving after a seven-day march from their village, which had been overrun by the Pathet Lao. They carried everything they owned on their backs. Our job was to treat and vaccinate them."

"The supply of medicines here is limited, not to mention equipment. But it amazes me how much you can do without X ray, a lab., electricity—or ice!"

"The doctor asked me if I thought I could stand it and I really didn't—I mean, the poor man's stomach was all torn open. But there was no one else to help, so I did."

"We receive the Bangkok *Post* three days late and there is a radio so we can hear the Voice of America and Radio Hanoi. Thus we are not completely cut off from the world."

These brave lines, chosen at random from some TADF volunteers' letters home, were written, not by the old hands, experienced enough to expect Asia's worst, but by a new breed of unpaid workers whose most trying times used to be precipitated by a spilled cup of coffee. Traveling Americans by the thousands have seen them on the nation's airlines, trim and lovely in immaculate stewardess uniforms and imbued with the glamor of anyone who flies regularly from coast to coast and continent to continent. Yet it is doubtful that their passengers would recognize any of these girls on Dooley Foundation duty. They wear whatever is coolest in Laos, whatever is warmest in the Himalayan foothills of India, and never mind how it looks. Their time is spent scrubbing scabrous children, collecting stool specimens, disinfecting maggoty latrines—any repugnant and thankless job that needs doing in some forbidding corner of the world. And nearly every one fights to get back for a second tour of service and the co-operating airlines, which grant successful applicants three to six months' leaves of absence, now maintain a waiting list of these aspiring short-term Dooley aides.

It began as a vague idea of Verne Chaney's to cope with the constant and sometimes crippling shortage of willing hands in the field. "We needed people to take the pressure off the doctors and nurses," he recalls. "They didn't have to be medically trained, only bright enough to see all the chores that had to be done and to do them without being told." The difficulty was a familiar one: he didn't have the resources to pay for such help, and certainly not to underwrite their transpacific flights.

Then, flying across the country one day on still another fund-raising drive, it suddenly occurred to Chaney that the pert stewardess who had just brought him a second cup of coffee without his asking was precisely the sort of person he wanted to plug the Dooley overseas personnel gap, and that she and her sister stewardesses and hostesses on all the airlines constituted a specially skilled labor pool from which he could keep the installations effectively staffed on a rotating basis—if only he could think of some way to attract them. Surely no group could be more natural Dooley ambassadors: they had youth, endurance, education and good looks; they were in constant contact with alien cultures, trained to anticipate needs and meet the unexpected with a smile.

He turned the idea over and over in his mind, testing and refining it. Then he called Sam Pryor, who had been a member of the TADF board of directors from the beginning, at Pan American Airways. Would Pan Am be willing to grant two- or three-month leaves to a few stewardess-volunteers? Yes. Good, and now could Pan Am fly them—and perhaps some from other airlines—to Asia on a space-available basis?

"You're not shy, are you, Verne?" Pryor said.

"It's a cruel world, Sam."

"I think we can handle it."

Not long after, Chaney telephoned a Pan Am stewardess based in San Francisco named Marleane Thompson. A mutual friend in Hong Kong had suggested they get together, he said. Perhaps they could have dinner. From cocktails to coffee, Chaney talked about the Dooley Foundation and its mission. This was always his tendency, but on that night he was watching closely for a reaction to his accounts of unrelieved sickness and poverty in Indochina, of Tibetan refugees struggling for existence in the barren sweep of northern India. When Marleane winced visibly at his calm recital of the Tibetan children's plight —many of them orphans, most of them putrid-smelling and covered with open sores because there was no one to teach them to wash—he was pretty sure he had found what he was looking for.

"It's a big problem," he said. "We need a lot of help."

"But what can one person do?" Marleane asked. "What could I do?"

"Well, now that you ask . . ." He leaned forward and put his elbows on the table. And he talked very earnestly to the girl he had decided would be the first stewardess-volunteer: "You can drive a truck, mop a dispensary floor, keep records, take temperatures, sew up the doctor's operating gown. If you've got any training at all you can give shots, do lab. analyses, assist at surgery. Do you have any feeling for kids? You can clean them up, teach them some hygiene, maybe a little English and just by being there give them the thing they want most of all—a sign that somebody out there in the wide world cares about them. Does that answer your question?"

"Yes."

"Listen, Marleane, a girl like you could do more good—for Asia *and* for America—than a battalion of Marines or a carload of medicine. How would you like to invest a couple of months of your life at it?"

"I would!" was the prompt reply. "And I'm pretty sure my roommate would, too."

On November 1, 1961, Pan Am stewardesses Marleane Thompson and Margery Burgy, having tacked a leave onto their own vacation time, arrived in New Delhi, and several uncertain days later came to Darjeeling, an Indian hill station on the Tibetan frontier. Here, where the British Sahibs had once sought refuge from the heat of the plains in summer, the Dalai Lama of Tibet had set up a seat of government for the 100,000 loyal subjects who had fled the Chinese Communists and followed him into exile. Now they were scattered across northern India, eking out a precarious livelihood on scattered road gangs, housed in improvised shelters and clothed in rags. Thousands had died on the long march over snowswept Himalayan passes, and thousands more in the harsh land where they'd sought freedom, and their children were cared for in refugee centers and makeshift orphanages.

With the help of the Indian government, Gyalo Thondup, brother of the Dalai Lama, had established a school and nursery for some 250 refugee children in Darjeeling. But there was so much to be done, so few skilled hands to do it and precious little to work with. Before Marleane and Marge came, the staff consisted of three Tibetan teachers who slept on the floor of the school and looked as hungry and tattered as the children. It was all they could do to keep their sad little charges from drifting off into hopeless lethargy.

"There was no question of asking anybody what to do," Marleane has said. "There was no one to ask. But the things that needed doing stared us right in the face."

Nervous and painfully aware of their shortcomings— fair and well-fed aliens in a bleak Asian land who knew nothing about teaching, medicine or the Tibetan language —they began by organizing a morning class in English and an afternoon dispensary. And the one thing they did have —uncritical affection—they gave in lavish abundance, and that alone launched the new Dooley project in the most promising way.

At first, sign language bridged the gap between English and Tibetan. But the children were extremely bright— "the brightest in the world" according to Marleane, as well as being "animated, charming, warm and courageous" —and, like sponges, they soaked up every word of instruction and were soon speaking quite respectable English sentences. The camp elders were so taken with the Dooley teachers and their good work that they gave them Tibetan names at a ceremony in the monastery presided over by a lama. Marleane became Gey Lhamoo-la, or Angel Goddess, and Marge was Gey Yang Chen-la, which means Goddess of Learning.

Coping with the children's physical needs called for considerably more resourcefulness than teaching the ABCs. None of them had shoes and the dirty old rags they wore fell apart at the touch. Their hair was long and tangled and infested with lice, their thin bodies covered with running abscesses that took weeks to heal, by which time the enforced filth with which they lived had done its work and a whole new rash of sores erupted elsewhere. Against this pervading squalor, the girls had at the start only a single cold water faucet to work with, some soap, one bottle of Lysol, a few disreputable bandages—and their innate ingenuity.

"After lunch one day we had the cooks warm water in their huge kettles and we stripped every one of those kids bare and gave them a bath," Marge recalls. "You could tell that most of them had never had soap on them before and they just danced with glee."

Thereafter the twice-weekly bath was an invariable part of the schedule, and once cleaned and bandaged, the ugly sores rapidly healed. The next challenge was the children's hair. Arming themselves with scissors and their own combs, Marleane and Marge hacked away at dark and dirt-encrusted thatches until they were short enough for an effective scrubbing, then topped their handiwork off by fashioning bangs for girls and boys alike, that being the only hairstyle they could do with any confidence. Later they managed to get combs for their children and each one treated it as a prized possession. "Hair-combing," Marleane reported, "became their favorite indoor and outdoor activity."

By pressure and pleading, the girls also got a room for their dispensary—they had no complaint about their own accommodations, sleeping bags in a corner of the schoolroom—and from New Delhi, a cabinet, table and a stock of basic medicines. There they bandaged skinned knees, administered aspirin for aches and pains, and held close the little ones who came out of loneliness for parents dead and gone forever, or those far away hammering rock on some frontier road.

At the end of six weeks, Marge Burgy fell ill and had to go home. Then Marleane was the only American woman in all Darjeeling, but she was much too busy to worry or even to feel unique. She doubled her classes, taught the children songs, basic health habits and a little arithmetic. It is a mark of her complete involvement that when Chaney came to assess the program and began taking pictures of her class in action, she resented his distracting her little students. She cleaned and trimmed fingernails, distributed vitamins whenever she could lay hands on them, sang and played games with the children, or just walked with them and was their friend. Somehow she wheedled a shipment of shoes and was able to fit about half the group. When an American tourist gave her a $10 donation, she bought some wool, taught the older girls to knit with needles made of bamboo sticks and in two weeks had 60 pairs of socks for the children.

Her leave was to have ended in mid-December and she had promised her family that she would surely be home for Christmas. But at the end of November she was cabling Pryor for a month's extension, and then in January for "just one more." And when, at last, she did have to leave, the day was the saddest of her life. "The children cried and I cried and when I started that long jeep ride to Bagdogra and the plane to Calcutta and San Francisco, it was exactly as though I'd left part of myself, part of my life behind."

She had also left an image of America and a faith in the essential goodwill of its people that no government agency could duplicate nor any foreign aid money buy. She has returned to India four times. Other stewardesses followed her to Darjeeling until, in the fall of 1962, it was closed to foreigners by the outbreak of Sino-Indian border fighting, and the next volunteers assigned to Tibetan refugee aid went to Mussoorie and Kathmandu, Nepal. But the children in Darjeeling are not forgotten. Thanks in large part to the start made by the Dooley Foundation and the subsequent attention drawn there, the refugee school is now regularly supplied and is well-staffed by Indian and Tibetan teachers and a qualified nurse.

Shirley Turner, a Canadian girl from Victoria, British Columbia, remembers reading one of Tom Dooley's books long before she went to work for United Air Lines in San Francisco. The next time she saw his name it changed her life. In the company magazine, she read about a United stewardess named Shirley Robinson who had gone to India under the auspices of the Thomas A. Dooley Foundation and spent three months helping to care for hundreds of Tibetan refugees. Almost the very next thing Shirley Turner did was call TADF and volunteer for the program. Then she began to haunt the library, reading books about India and Tibet and studying maps of the Himalayan frontier until she could all but see its great peaks vanishing in clouds, and the isolated little towns where orphan children huddled against the cold and eagerly awaited the compassion and companionship of some new American stewardess. Then Chaney sent for Shirley and said she would be going to Ban Houei Sai in Laos.

"I was stunned," she remembers. "I had no idea where that place was. I couldn't even pronounce it. Working with children was one thing—I felt I could do that—but with no medical training I didn't know what earthly use I'd be in a hospital."

She found out soon enough. Reaching her destination early in March, 1964, she had a panoramic view of the place that was to be her home for the next two months as the pilot twice buzzed the compound to signal their arrival. There was a flurry of activity below, then a dark-haired girl detached herself from the waving cluster of people on the hospital steps, climbed aboard a red Honda and with a long trail of dust spewing behind, raced them to the grassy airstrip. Then Shirley Turner was greeted with words familiar to nearly every TADF newcomer.

"Hi," said nurse Ann Kidder. "We weren't expecting you—crippled communications around here—but there's sure plenty for you to do!"

Two hours later, having been introduced to the staff— Bob Conway was the doctor then, Barry Seeley the aide— and taken on a whirlwind tour of the hospital, she was doing it. There were long-deferred letters to type, a small medical library and office to organize and clothes to be mended for staff members who were too busy building latrines to have much time for needle and thread. Asked to make face masks for the operating room, she rummaged around until she'd found some gauze and a few old sheets, washed them, cut them to size and sewed them to satisfactory thickness. She solved the problem of how to tie them around the head by stitching lengths of seam tape to the masks' four corners. And where did the seam tape come from?

"The inside of my dresses," Shirley reports with a wry smile. "I looked around that place and knew darn well I had no need for fancy clothes."

When she had caught up with all the chores accumulated for her, she plunged into the countless routine tasks that had to be done every day—taking temperatures, cleaning and wrapping instruments for autoclaving, comforting the older patients and amusing the small ones. She was so busy in fact that two weeks passed before she realized she'd completely forgotten to stay disappointed at not being assigned to India.

"There were other compensations," she has said. "Slowly it dawned on me that this was Tom Dooley's own place, the last hospital he'd built. Here was Oi, whose life Dooley had saved and who was now our cook. This was the house Dooley lived in, the table he sat at, and down the hill the same Mekong River and those magnificent sunsets he must have loved. How could anybody who cared about his work not be grateful to be here?"

Oi, the cook at the TADF hospital in Ban Houei Sai, was a legacy. Five years before, when he was perhaps fourteen, crippled by an old injury and feverish with typhoid, he had been carried to Muong Sing by his family and left on the hospital steps. Then the family disappeared. Dooley did what had to be done, as always: he cured the fever, corrected the deformity in the leg with surgery, and then, because the boy had no place to go, made a place for him at Muong Sing. He taught him to speak English and cook, and since then Oi had been at one Dooley hospital or another.

Shirley, happy to be where Dooley had been, missed neither the absence of tangible rewards nor the scarcity of creature comforts at Houei Sai. Once she got over her astonishment, she could laugh at—and learned to love— the "shower," a rain barrel and a hand dipper. In time she got used to the Asian john, a straddle trench that had to be manually flushed, and even quit worrying about the water, which was hauled up by oxcart from the muddy Mekong, that community bath and laundry for all the river villages between China and the South China Sea. For drinking, they purified it with halazone pills.

But she only went once to the morning market. Oi woke her at 5 A.M.—"We go now soon before all best meat gone!"—and when they arrived in town an hour later a lively crowd had already gathered around the wooden stalls of fish, meat and fresh vegetables. For a while Shirley thought it the most colorful spectacle she had ever seen— carts of still-arriving produce dumped into sidewalk bins, Lao housewives bantering and bargaining with vendors who sat crosslegged beside their wares—and she moved merrily around gawking and snapping pictures.

Then she made the mistake of coming too close to the meat stall where the separate parts of oxen and water buffalo—tails, hooves, heads, intestines—were graphically laid out and swarming with flies.

"From this grand array Oi had selected the meat for our dinner," she was to write home, "and I suddenly forgot how good he could make food taste and saw only those huge heads staring back at me."

By evening, however, the savory smell of frying "buffaloburgers" easily overcame her lingering qualms and she ate heartily. "I just never went back to the market, that's all."

One day, with no warning, there were the battle casualties. The first ones came on a Sunday when Ann and the Lao nurses had gone into town. Suddenly a helicopter thundered to a landing and there they were, one with his stomach laid open and the other with both hands blown off. Shirley ran all the way to the clinic and got there just as Dr. Conway was ordering the man with the mangled stomach to the operating room.

"What can I do?" she asked at once.

"Go with that guy," the doctor replied crisply as he turned his attention to the dried and dirty stumps at the end of the second man's wrists. "I want you to take a good look at his guts. If you can stand it I'll need your help until the others get back. If you can't, go find yourself some smelling salts and take a long walk."

Alone in the operating room with the wounded man, Shirley looked. One part of her brain calmly deduced that he must have been bayoneted. The other shrieked a message of protest and horror to the rest of her body and she had to fight to keep from fleeing. A jagged 6-inch rent had exposed all his intestines, some of which had fallen out of the stomach cavity and writhed and churned bloodily with an agony of their own. His genitals were partly torn off.

Shirley grew dizzy. She is sure she would have vomited, perhaps even fainted, if she had not become aware that the man was staring intently at her. His pain dulled by drugs, he remained alert enough to know that this American girl had seen the worst and he searched her face for some sign of how critically he was hurt. Steeling herself, remembering that for now at least there was no one else to help Dr. Conway, she smiled at the sweating Lao and began to wipe up the blood that had dripped to the floor.

Conway took time for only a quick, "Good work," when he hurried into the operating room, then began directing her through the whole series of pre-operative procedures—laying out the instruments, helping him scrub up and get into his gown and mask, preparing the patient. She was actually standing by to assist in the surgery, the fact that she had no medical training forgotten, when Ann Kidder rushed in. She had heard the helicopter, deduced its mission and begged a ride back from town. The Lao aides were on their way, too, she reported.

Conway stole a moment to tell Shirley his thanks. "You're a good girl," he said, and her heart swelled with pride. "Now go look after the other guy until we're ready for him. He needs a urinal and I'm pretty sure it's been a couple of days since he's had anything to eat."

The other Lao lay propped up on a bed, his truncated forearms folded uselessly across his chest. He had been holding a grenade in his hands when it exploded—seven days before. Then he had been carried to the helicopter pickup and now the sight and smell of him had driven other patients to the farthest corner of the room. Shirley drew a curtain around him and brought the urinal.

"I don't know how I got through that," she says. "But it helped to remember that it was a lot worse for that poor man than it was for me."

Because he seemed too weak to chew, she made a "milk-shake" of high protein powder, sugar and water, and held it to his lips as he sipped eagerly. Then she just sat with him, uncertain of what else to do and hoping that her presence would somehow reassure him. And so she sat three hours until Dr. Conway was ready for him—it had taken more than 300 sutures to close the other patient's stomach wounds—and then she went out into the fading sunlight and leaned against the building and cried.

On the day before Shirley was to leave for home, King

Savang Vathana and the Queen came to visit Houei Sai. For days everyone in the town was busy painting, repairing and decorating and it occurred to Shirley that this would be a likely time to distribute the trunk full of used clothing her friends at home had sent for the patients she'd written about, as well as most of her own dresses, which she'd decided to leave for them as well. In order not to hurt anyone's pride, she simply took the clothes down to the ward in a big box, indicating it was for the patients if they wanted them, and then left. When she went back later, the box was empty and the ward was in turmoil as men and women tried on their new possessions, traded them for better fits and happily preened and paraded themselves from one end of the room to the other. Perhaps the King was puzzled the next day as he inspected the Dooley hospital to see the patients in Western clothing. But it was generally agreed that they were a distinct improvement over the tatters most had worn when they arrived.

Shirley flew home at the end of April, but her links to TADF remain strong. She wrote an instruction booklet for future Asia-bound stewardesses, then toured the other installations to prepare for a new assignment: director of volunteers in San Francisco. And often her thoughts drift back to the place called Ban Houei Sai, and sometimes it is almost as though she were there again, so deeply is it impressed in her heart.

Joan Hvezda, an Eastern Airlines stewardess, volunteered for TADF's short-term volunteer program in the early summer of 1966 and was assigned to Khong Island.

Then as in a delayed reaction she suddenly realized how far from her home in Rosemont, New Jersey, she'd come and how absolutely primitive Khong was. One night a typical monsoon rain exploded overhead and she woke with water pouring, not dripping, through the roof. Before she could move, her bed was drenched. Another night she went to bed before the generator had been shut down so there was still light in her room—and saw a swarm of cockroaches scurrying across the sheet. She realized at once that they must have been there the night before and the night before that and screamed with such uncontrollable ferocity that everyone in the staff quarters came running, Pat Patipatanakoon with an upraised frying pan for an improvised club. She worried about getting sick and was unnerved by the fact that news from anywhere was three weeks old and began to have regrets about the whole thing.

Then, as quickly as the depression had come on her, and as unaccountably, it passed. "I shooed the chickens out of the kitchen, brushed the cockroaches out of my bed and decided that with the state of the world that summer, what was the big rush to hear the news? *Bo pin yan?* What's the difference? I had a job to do and *that* was important."

Some notes from a journal she kept during her three months in Laos suggest how important it was:

"June 14. Assigned to make ward rounds with medicine four times a day. Sometimes I get to talking with the patients—a little Lao, a lot of sign language—and am still there when it's time for the next round. But I think they feel better when one of us is around.

"June 18. I have tonsillitis, of all things. Dr. Davia says I'll be up and around in a couple of days. But my big thrill was when one of the patients came to see *me*. She wanted to know what was wrong and would touch my foot and arm and say, '*Chep? Chep?*' meaning, was that what hurt. How do you say sore throat in Lao?

"June 28. A distraught mother stood on the doorstep in the middle of the night holding a screaming baby. She had been walking since early morning. The child's ear was swollen and some horrible-looking black magic potion had been smeared over his head. Dr. Davia and I never did get back to bed. We worked over the baby by flashlight, forcing medicine into him, and by daybreak the fever seemed broken.

"June 29. Took the boat to a village with Marge (Alberding) to attend a pregnant woman. The child was born dead. Returned home to find a crowd at the door. A Chinese from town had sawed off three of his fingers and was bleeding very badly. I helped Dr. Davia administer anesthesia and assisted at the surgery. It took two and a half hours and we finished by candlelight. For the rest of the night, between catnaps, I fed our sick baby and gave him medicine.

"July 2. The baby went home today, all better. We think the mother has learned a lot about feeding, bathing and caring for him. Boy, would I have loved to take that little guy home!"

Before she returned to the United States, Joan was thoroughly familiar with all the frustrations that plagued the oldest hands—the supplies that didn't arrive, the countless maddening obstructions of the witch doctors and the seeming indifference of the people to their own sickness. Why should they boil drinking water? Their fathers hadn't. Their grandfathers hadn't. But she came away, too, with the same glimmer of hope brought home by every Dooley volunteer. She remembers, "Dr. Chi or

Dr. Davia would say, 'No your father didn't boil water, but how long did he live? How often was he in pain?' And a glimmer of understanding would come into their eyes and you could actually believe you'd made a little headway."

There was a *baci* in her honor before she left, and many strings tied around her wrists. And an old crone who knew of Joan's affection for the baby she'd nursed back to health two months before offered for her the most touching wish of all. "She hopes for you," Dr. Chi translated with some embarrassment as the woman tied the string, "a Lao baby in your stomach."

From its speculative beginnings at the end of 1961, the stewardess program has grown into a strong and integral part of the entire TADF endeavor. More than 150 volunteers from nine co-operating domestic and one foreign airline have now served in Southeast Asia under Dooley auspices, and the names of new applicants are forwarded to San Francisco every day. And though their experiences and reactions are naturally quite different, all the girls took away as much in understanding and insight as they gave in service.

In greater or lesser degree, they shared too a sort of culture shock to actually find themselves in such strange and remote lands. One girl flying over the immense rain forests of Vietnam imagined snakes and tigers in their brooding midsts—and only long after realized that thousands of people lived there too. But they learned and adjusted and each, within her limits, contributed something to the continuing war on poverty, ignorance and ill-health.

Mildred Adams, a stewardess on the plane that brought Tom Dooley home to die, went to Kathmandu, Nepal, to do what she called "sidewalk nursing" among Tibetan refugees, and now says, "I never knew what it might mean to be something less than a well-fed, comfortably-off American, and I never would have found out if I hadn't joined the Dooley program. You can't *learn* that kind of thing from a newspaper."

TADF volunteer Nancy Williams heard that United Air Lines was changing stewardesses' uniforms and launched a "Tibetan trousseaus" campaign, rounded up 2,000 outdated skirts and jackets and took them to India for distribution among the refugees. "That was foreign aid person-to-person," she says, "and it was as meaningful to all of us who helped a little as it was to the Tibetans. They appreciate government help, certainly, but governments don't have faces."

But perhaps no one came closer to explaining what the stewardess program can mean to the volunteers than did Marleane Thompson, the first one. "It's not the usual kind of vacation," she once wrote. "You won't meet some charming young man. Instead of a suntan, you'll probably come home with dysentery. But it will give special value to your life, which is more than you can say for any two weeks at the beach."

CHAPTER VII

The Purdys

SUSAN AND PETER PURDY, first married couple to join the Dooley Foundation, celebrated one wedding anniversary in Ban Houei Sai, Laos, and another in Mussoorie, India. This continued to perplex their friends and relatives who had not understood the young couple's urge to go to the other side of the world "to help" in the first place. While others planned families and future, Peter and Susan wrote letters to philanthropic organizations with overseas interests. While old school mates paid off auto and television installments, Peter and Susan saved every spare dollar so they could, if necessary, pay their own passage to whatever far corner of the earth they were sent.

Susan, an honor graduate of the University of California, had worked for *Time* in New York, then gone traveling in Europe. "I wanted to see something of the world besides the east and west coasts of the United States," she has said.

Peter had a journalism degree from the University of Minnesota and was in Europe "through the courtesy of the U.S. Army." He was disturbed by the reflections he sometimes saw of the American image. "It was bad enough talking to foreigners who were dead wrong in their estimates of my country," he says. "But all too often they were right—that though the American government showed concern for less fortunate nations, Americans as individuals seemed indifferent to less fortunate people—and that hurt."

In 1963 they sent an application to TADF, then went to San Francisco for an interview with Chaney. They left for Asia in July, bound first for a brief period of orientation at Houei Sai, and afterwards for teaching posts among the Tibetan refugees in northern India where they were to survey the needs of three Tibetan schools. This is an excerpt from their report:

"The children have meat but once a week, no eggs, no fresh fruit. Vegetables consist of onions and potatoes, but the basic ration is rice, wheat and *dahl*, a warm and filling lentil soup. Medicaments are at a minimum. In none of the schools does anyone have warm jackets or sweaters. Out of the 300 children here, fewer than 50 have shoes and no one has underwear of any kind. Personal toilet articles are nonexistent. At one school, 54 boys sleep on the cement floor and all use the same towel and the same comb. They all have blankets, but being in the mountains, it is very cold here at night."

Despite these privations, despite the loneliness of being separated from their parents, the children made no complaint. Once, though, the Purdys visited a nursery where fifty little ones, pathetic in their craving for a little affection, came toward them with arms outstretched in a silent appeal to be picked up. Older ones looked after the tots as best they could and all clung tenaciously to their culture and religion, standing straight and tall to sing the Tibetan anthem every morning and night.

One day, Susan and Peter had a chance to see the reunion of some parents and their children. Mothers and fathers alike worked on the road gangs and had walked many miles from their camp to visit the children. "It was very moving," Susan recalls. "There was no wild rejoicing, just quiet talk. And before long, because they had such a long way to go, the parents prepared to leave, giving each child a kiss and a two-rupee note, which represented half a day's wages."

So the young Americans came early to an understanding of the Tibetan character—gentle, forbearing, brave. Nearly every one of the refugees had lost a loved one, either at the hands of the Communists or on the long trek over the Himalayas. But they lived their religion, a first precept of which holds that suffering exists, and patiently endured their misfortune, and hoped, with their compassionate leader, for happier days. "If it is 100 or 150 years before my people return to their country, then I am prepared for this," the Dalai Lama has said. "My hope rests in the courage of Tibetans and the love of truth and justice which is still in the heart of the human race."

With the Purdys' report in hand, Verne Chaney authorized an expenditure of 2,500 rupees, about $525, on behalf of the children, and Susan and Peter set out on a shopping spree such as they had never more enjoyed. They bought 30 triple-decker beds, 250 pairs of shoes and a two-months' supply of soap; sheets, towels, some basic medicines, toothbrushes and combs; school exercise books, pencils, bamboo pens, ink and some kerosene lamps. When they found they still had a few dollars left over, they bought sacks of oranges and distributed them on the spot. "I wish," wrote Peter to Chaney, "that everyone who ever made a contribution to the Dooley Foundation could have seen those kids' faces when the stuff began coming in. They would have been rewarded tenfold."

Learning of the Purdys' work, the Dalai Lama asked to see them and they prepared for the audience with nervous bustle. But they found him to be a man of deep humanity and gentle humor—"You have captured our children's hearts; please do not take them away with you"—and were soon talking easily about life in the United States and their own experiences. And obviously His Holiness was gladdened by the young Americans' keen sense of mission, for it was he who suggested what was to be their permanent TADF assignment, the Tibetan refugee schools in Mussoorie, and he whose influence smoothed many of their problems.

Mussoorie is a one-time British hill station in Uttar Pradesh province, 170 miles north of New Delhi. There, some 1,200 refugee children were housed, half in government schools and the other half in the twenty-five foster homes run by the Tibetan Homes Foundation. This remarkable institution, supported by private funds from England, Switzerland, Canada and the U.S., was headed by a remarkable human being. Mrs. Rinchen Dolma (Precious Goddess) Taring, a member of Tibet's aristocracy and first Tibetan woman to be educated outside that land, was married to the former heir to the throne of Sikkim. Susan and Peter warmed to her at once and listened, captivated, to her stories of the Chinese onslaught and of Tibetan resistance and suffering. Not for some days, though, could she bring herself to tell them how two of her own three daughters were captured trying to escape and forced into coolie labor by the Communists. Now her life was devoted to easing the way for other Tibetan children driven to an unfamiliar land, and to helping them preserve their heritage and age-old culture against the time when they would be free to go home. She helped the Purdys organize two classes of fifty children each, for whom there had been no room at the Indian school. The language barrier was quickly overcome by the inherent brightness of the new students and by their great eagerness to learn. Starting with only a portable blackboard and a pocketful of chalk, Susan and Peter taught simple words, which soon became sentences, and these turned into paragraphs with real meaning for the children. And all at once they were communicating.

"I don't know who got more out of it," Peter says, "those kids, to learn English, or Susan and I, suddenly to realize we could talk to them and reach them and carry them right along with us, no matter what we decided to try."

As a little money became available, they bought pencils and copybooks. They taught simple arithmetic, worked basic lessons in personal hygiene into grammar studies, organized spelling bees with postcards and postage stamps as prizes—and felt themselves constantly pushed by the children's intensity to expand the scope of studies. Susan formed an advanced class of older pupils and taught them to think and reason, a technique ignored in the Asian education system, which seems based largely on rote. She found herself staying up late each night to prepare lessons for these just-awakened young minds, quick to devour everything she had to teach—the history of India, World War II, Buddhism—and then yearned for more. Even during the wildest monsoon rains the children came to class, arriving soaking wet, shivering by the tin stove as they dried out while the lessons went on.

School papers, in awkward and sometimes self-conscious English, always reflected their inner thoughts:

"My town has many Chinese soldiers. They were cheated to us. They cannot go to heaven."

"The Dalai Lama is the great of Tibetans. The world respect him muchly."

"I never forget my country Tibet. We never like Chinese Communists so they must one day go."

"The Lord Buddha don't like luxury."

All the children shared a lively sense of humor. One boy was nicknamed "Horse" and when he was absent from school one day Susan asked if anyone knew where he was. Tsewang stood up and very respectfully said, "He ask excuse me. He has gone for grazing."

Though they knew little about the outside world, their instincts and reactions were not unlike those of children everywhere. When his team lost an improvised and hard-fought game roughly approximating soccer, one lad complained to Peter that they'd been done in only because of "the dishonest of the whistler."

In Mussoorie the Purdys lived in a two-room stone cottage close to Foster Homes 6 and 7, where fifty of the little Tibetan refugees lived. Late in the afternoon, when classes were over for the day, their sitting room was invariably packed with children drawing in coloring books, playing checkers, working on jigsaw puzzles or just sitting there, quietly content to be close to their American teachers. Sometimes they broke into spirited Tibetan dances, in which Susan and Peter joined, and taught the children, in return, such hectic Western gyrations as the twist and the jerk.

The house sat on a mountainside at the edge of a pine forest. Four thousand feet below was a broad valley, and across, the eternally snow-covered Himalayas. Tibet was less than 100 miles away. In summer it was a beautiful place, cool and fresh and brightened by the daisies and orchids and dahlias that grew wild all around them. In winter it was freezing cold. They had a tin stove in the sitting room, but the bedroom was known as the ice chamber. Susan catalogued their sleeping gear in a letter home: "Seven blankets, sleeping bags, Tibetan carpets, long underwear and, in January, the coldest month, even gloves and hats."

There were bears and panthers in the forest, but they never saw them. The monkeys, however, were there constantly, sometimes using their tin roof as a springboard to the surrounding trees, and curious enough to come right in the house if they left the door open. One day they came home to find three in their bedroom, carefully going through the closet. But the monkeys were a joy compared to their problems with scorpions, immense spiders and rats. And the worst problem of all was that they couldn't kill them when the children were around—which was nearly always—because the Buddhist creed forbids the taking of life. They had no choice but to adopt a "peaceable kingdom" attitude. "But I can't honestly say that we learned to love our rats," reports Peter.

Somehow the Purdys came to be acknowledged as experts in solving any problem—mechanical, technical, organizational—by Mrs. Taring and her staff at the Tibetan Homes Foundation. Coming from the highly specialized

Western world, this unsettled them at first, but they soon came to realize that they were invested as "experts," not because they knew how to do everything, but because they knew where to find out how to do it. And since there was a great deal to be done over and above their teaching assignments they accepted the title and did the work. They dug garbage pits for Homes 6 and 7, organized a library, encouraged Tibetan artisans to continue fashioning their unique handicrafts, then built a shop to sell them.

The library was Peter's special project. He began with a few volumes in a single room at the school and some evenings of research into the Dewey decimal system for classifying books and periodicals. Then he got busy writing letters to friends for book contributions, and to a whole range of American magazines for free subscriptions. The response was gratifying. A high school sophomore in Edina, Minnesota, Peter's home town, collected 300 fine books, then solved the problem of how to get them to India by persuading the school Red Cross chapter to undertake the shipping as a special project. As his collection grew, Peter trained a young Tibetan teacher as librarian and on a most auspicious day, the new library opened with appropriate ceremony, tea and *kapsay*, a sweet Tibetan pastry.

Susan was particularly fascinated by the newly built Tibetan Buddhist temple in Mussoorie. With the help of Mr. and Mrs. Taring and Rinpoche, the incarnate lama, she came to know a great deal about its paintings, symbolic of Tibetan belief. One day she decided that their beauty and significance would be greatly enhanced for visitors if they could have available the information she had gleaned over the course of many visits. And so she sat down and wrote out the story of the temple, describing the basic Buddhist beliefs depicted there. When she showed it to Jamyang, the lama who had done the intricate painting on the walls and ceilings, he set to work doing illustrations to go with her manuscript. From friends in the States she collected enough money to have text and pictures printed and bound in a small pamphlet, and these were placed in the temple for anyone to read or to take away. "The Tibetans I knew worked so hard, and with so little, to hang onto their art and costumes and songs and, most importantly, their religion," Susan says. "I am very proud of that pamphlet because I think it helps a little to perpctuate their culture."

Long after the youngest of the children is grown up and gone, the Tibetan refugees in Mussoorie will remember Susan and Peter Purdy for the handicraft shop they started. Almost from their arrival, the Americans realized that there was a considerable number of Tibetans in the area who were highly skilled in the ancient crafts of their homeland—bootmaking, painting, weaving, embroidery. Even in exile they continued to work and to produce articles of rare beauty and usefulness. But unhappily they didn't know what to do with them in this strange new place, for there was no market where they could be displayed, no one in Mussoorie who seemed to be interested in buying Tibetan handicrafts. Sometimes they would stop by the Purdys' cottage and ask them to sell some of their things because they needed money for food, and Peter and Susan would take their silver lamps and scrolls and beautifully made boots to New Delhi and get good prices for them in the American community.

"But that sort of thing was limited and couldn't go on for long anyway," Susan has said. "Peter and I felt so sorry for these marvelous craftsmen who had depended on their skills for a livelihood, and now what were they to do?"

When it dawned on her, as well, that without demand or outlets for their wares the artisans would soon have no incentive to continue working and that this unique Tibetan art would be lost forever, she decided that something had to be done about it.

"I'm going to start a handicraft shop," she announced to Peter one day.

"A what?"

"A handicraft shop. A place where the people can sell those beautiful things they make. And then I'm going out and drum up some business for them."

Peter said he thought that was a noble idea, but what, he logically asked, did she know about selling handicrafts, where would she find a place to start such a shop, and who was going to put up the money to get it off the ground?

"I don't know," was her inclusive answer, "but that's no reason not to do it. There has to be a way."

And of course there was. For 90 rupees a year ($19), she rented a small wooden stall at the bazaar—that was the shop. With 263 rupees ($55) which she pried out of TADF headquarters, she bought some things from Mr. Norbu, the bootmaker, and Mr. Chakshamba, the painter. Adding only a small margin to their purchase price and stealing a few hours out of her teaching schedule to display the handicrafts in the bazaar, she had no trouble selling them to tourists, whereupon she put all the money back into the acquisition of more stock. As word of the shop's modest success spread, craftsmen from New Delhi and Dharamsala, came to ask if they could display their wood carvings and embroidery there too, as, later, did two Tibetan crafts co-operatives which were having trouble finding outlets in Dalhousie.

Susan said Yes to one and all and soon her shelves bulged with a whole range of fine Tibetan handwork. Nor was there any shortage of customers: Embassy friends from Delhi, students who visited Mussoorie and teachers from a private school across the valley all came to look and stayed to buy. Peter, by now thoroughly infected with Susan's enthusiasm, made up a mail-order list of available articles and sent them to every TADF chapter in the United States. The response was stunning.

And every penny of income went into the purchase of still more stock, which was of course a financial blessing to the craftsmen and artisans who supplied it. Then Susan hired a bright young Tibetan named Kunjo to run the shop while she moved on to another, equally important phase of the operation.

She had been thinking about Mr. Norbu, who was once royal bootmaker in Lhasa and painstakingly fashioned boots for all the nobility. His work was magnificent, red wool felt attached to the heavy leather sole with an embroidered braid, with exquisitely embroidered Tibetan designs from ankle to knee. She mentioned it to Peter— "It's a shame that such an art has to die when Mr. Norbu goes"—and he came up with the next exciting idea: with TADF support, Mr. Norbu, his wife, and a skilled sole maker were put on salary to conduct classes for forty children in the intricate art of leatherwork, bootmaking, and embroidery. "I feel very good," said Susan to Peter at the conclusion of the handicraft school's opening ceremonies. "I feel as though we have had a hand in preserving something quite special for the world."

Nor were they finished. The handicraft booth, begun in April, 1964, by October was so busy and cramped for space that when Susan pointed out the need for a proper shop, Peter said, "I've been thinking about it for a week."

There was much to think about. Their best estimates of cost for even a small building was around $2,000 which, given its medical commitments, they did not think they could ask the Foundation to provide. So they decided to raise it themselves. Peter began by writing articles for newspapers back home, payment for which went into the building fund, and letters to TADF chapters asking them to contribute to this special project. Together they made a list of family and friends in the States who might be interested and sent each one a request for help.

The chapters responded promptly and generously, particularly those in Arlington, Massachusetts, and Minneapolis-St. Paul, and soon there was enough money—and the Purdys' firm faith that the rest would be provided—to start construction. Each day they were on hand to see the little white building take shape, 15 by 17 feet, with sliding door cabinets and decorated with gay curtains. In December the contractor was nearly finished and began pointedly asking for the balance of the money due him. Some desperate times followed as the Purdys racked their brains for a way out of the dilemma.

"It'll take a miracle," said Susan glumly.

And the miracle—Christmas—was forthcoming. Day by day, stacks of greetings cards from friends in America were delivered to the stone cottage on the hill, nearly everyone containing a contribution for the new handicraft shop. "Amazing and wonderful," Peter kept saying. "The best Christmas present anyone could have sent."

There was enough money to pay the contractor, and

enough left to cast a plaque for the front of the building which said:

TIBETAN HANDICRAFT SHOP
BUILT THROUGH THE EFFORT OF
THE THOMAS A. DOOLEY FOUNDATION
JANUARY 1, 1965.

"It's true," says Peter, "that the money actually came from individuals. But it was the Dooley Foundation that sent us here and backed us and made the whole thing possible."

There remained a great deal to be done. The shop floor was still, in Susan's words, "good old Mother Earth" and there was need for more cupboards, chairs and a stove.

But the Purdys went on shamelessly begging contributions and the new Tibetan Handicraft Shop opened on schedule, February 26, 1965. Then the shop and Mr. Norbu's craft center were joined under the name Tibetan Projects with Mrs. Taring in charge, and all profits were assigned to the children's foster homes to buy fresh fruit and meat.

And Susan and Peter Purdy—who with a single vigorously pursued idea had already restored the pride of dozens of Tibetan artisans and provided them with a regular income—kept right on working. With expanded facilities, they reached out for an expanded market. And again Eastern craftsmanship and Western know-how were blended to provide a sensational breakthrough.

"You know," said Peter one evening, "if those boots of Norbu's were cut down from knee to ankle length they'd be great for after-ski wear."

Susan reacted at once. "That's right!" she exclaimed and bolted straight up in her chair. "And there are some other things . . ."

In an hour they had listed half a dozen typically Tibetan products that, with only slight adaptation, would surely appeal to Western tastes. Thick bolts of handwoven cloth were lovely but hardly practical—but what if they were cut in 12-inch squares and fringed for place mats? Many weavers made handsome bootstraps for only a handful of people, but suppose they used the same skills and native materials to make headbands and matching belts?

The craftsmen went enthusiastically to work and the Purdys began broadening their markets in New Delhi and, through the TADF chapters, among retail stores in the States. Success was heady indeed, sometimes too much so, as when an American shoe chain ordered 100 pairs of "after-ski" boots: working at top speed, Norbu could only produce 15 pairs a month. By the time the Purdys had to leave Mussoorie, the handicraft shop was firmly established and flourishing, its initial capital value increased tenfold, and the craft center assured that there would continue to be skilled artisans to carry on this uniquely Tibetan tradition.

Glory House in Dharamsala, was home base for the two mobile health units presented by TADF for the care of Tibetan refugees. Clinics were held there for people from the town and nearby camps, and regularly the huge van and trailer would rumble out to the farther sites, roaming the mountainous land for weeks at a time to bring diagnosis, treatment and medicine to some 10,000 road workers in a bleak area of 30,000 square miles.

The eight-member medical team included two women, Tibetan nurse Sonam Dhondup and, from April, 1964 to

May, 1965, Dooley Foundation volunteer Vernell Geist-weidt. Both did their fair share of pushing the trailer along precarious, mile-high roads when the turns were so sharp and the paths so narrow that the jeep had to be disconnected. They slogged through miles of mud and snow, slept shivering in sleeping bags when the temperature dropped to 20 below zero, held their breath when rock-slides pounded their vehicles and threatened to obliterate them—and fought a stubborn, endless battle against the diseases that preyed on an undernourished people who lived in ragged tents and labored long hours at the most back-breaking work.

Most often they located a distant camp by the prayer flags strung from some height and flapping vigorously in the endless wind. Then the gray tents would come into view, and the workers, all of whom ran to cluster around the van or trailer, for nearly all needed medical aid. Intestinal parasites, skin eruptions, vitamin deficiencies and respiratory infections were the most common ills. Tuberculosis, virtually unknown in Tibet so that the people had developed no natural resistance, now struck their crowded, unsanitary little camps with particular ferocity.

Once the TADF team found their way blocked by a huge boulder, so they packed their medicines and walked six miles to their destination. Another time they came to a stream where the bridge had washed out and rather than turn back they rebuilt it themselves. It took them two days. Sometimes, though, when the road ahead had been soaked and slicked by pounding rains and there was a catastrophic drop just beyond the edge of the outer wheels, they wondered if they mightn't skip just one camp. They never did.

"You just can't bring yourself to do it," says nurse

Geistweidt. "One of those times, we went to the camp and, besides all the usual sickness, we found a man with a hemoglobin of 20 per cent, passing bloody urine and generally so debilitated that had we not gotten him back to the hospital he almost surely would have died within the week."

Sometimes all their efforts were heartbreakingly in vain. In January, there was a dynamiting accident in one of the camps injuring several workers. TADF arranged hospital care for them, then received word that a special and very costly medicine was required to save the eyesight of one young man. They provided it. Soon after, a second expensive medicine was needed, and again TADF bought it. Still the man's vision failed and it was ultimately decided that the only chance to save it would be to send him to the Ludhiana Christian Medical College Hospital in central Punjab for a corneal transplant. The Dooley Foundation undertook to bear the expenses of the trip, for which the man's wife and father expressed tearful gratitude. TADF took him by jeep to Pathankot, arranged for an escort to go with him the rest of the way and paid both their fares to Ludhiana—where the ophthalmologist in charge made a painstaking examination and announced that they had come too late: nothing could be done to ward off inevitable blindness.

Vernell Geistweidt returned home in the spring, but an Indian-Tibetan team, supported by the Dooley Foundation, works on. Only recently nurse Dhondup reported, "We still move from camp to camp attending the sick people, but we have opened a few camp dispensaries and hope to open more in order to spread preventive medicine. No words can say how important the Dooley Foundation is to the Tibetan refugee road workers, no one can tell their thanks."

Susan and Peter Purdy often performed liaison chores between TADF headquarters and the mobile health clinic in Dharamsala, but their real work was in Mussoorie, and their hearts belonged to the refugee children there. Because they felt honored to participate and knew it would please the little ones, they attended prayer services at the temple and carried smoking pine branches to the top of the Himalayan foothills to commemorate Buddhist holidays. On Uprising Day the children put on a play marking the final defiance of the Tibetan people. On that date in 1959, when the Chinese demanded that the Dalai Lama come to their Embassy, his subjects, fearing His Holiness would be abducted or harmed, surrounded the Patola Palace and shouted warnings urging him not to leave. This, and happier scenes remembered from life in Tibet, were poignantly reenacted by the youngsters.

As the Christmas season approached, the Purdys explained its religious and festive significance to their classes —though there were some children who remained convinced that Jesus and Santa Claus were one and the same. A happy group of them helped Peter choose and cut a tree and that evening sat breathless and expectant as Susan decorated it with tin can tops, colored toilet paper rolls, paper yaks and cardboard candy canes. When the great day came, all fifty of their children crowded into the Purdys' cottage, leaving barely enough room for a race in which they pushed peanuts across the floor with their noses, balloon-bursting relays and—favorite game of all— Pin the Tail on the Yak.

After hot chocolate and cookies, Peter read *The Night Before Christmas* by candlelight. Then he said, "Now if you all sing 'Jingle Bells' very, very loudly, I think you'll have a special surprise."

They made the rafters ring with "Jingle all the wa-ay,"

and at the climactic moment, who should come bursting through the door but the merry old gentleman himself, Santa Claus—magnificently impersonated by an English friend of the Purdys who'd had the foresight to bring his red suit and cotton beard—laden with gifts for all! The children squealed and danced with transported delight, and Susan would later say, "I suppose comparisons are unfair, but I just couldn't help wondering if the millions of fabulous toys given to American kids that day were as gratefully received as the used washcloths and pencils we managed to collect."

In March, both Susan and Peter fell ill with infectious hepatitis and were sent to the mission hospital. There, on St. Patrick's Day—Peter's birthday—a sizeable delegation of their little pupils came to sing "Happy Birthday" and present the patients with homemade get-well cards. A typical one said, "I am praying to the God every day to all right your sickness."

Early the following month, the Purdys, shaky and thin and moved close to tears, bade goodbye to the children and all their friends in Mussoorie and set out on the long journey home.

"How can we ever sum up such an experience?" Susan has said. "We learned so much, mostly that you can't help people as well as they can help themselves, and that with only a little encouragement and guidance, they will. And our Asian friends learned that Americans are not so different from them, maybe a little luckier so far, that's all."

And Peter, who came to believe deeply in the TADF credo of person-to-person help, entered the University of California in the fall to study for a masters degree in international public relations, his eye on a career as an administrator in private-aid projects. "I learned the great

value of this kind of help from the Dooley Foundation,"
he says. "You are free to move, to *do*. You see a need and
you meet it without having to go back to some government bureau for policy decisions and permission. Tom
Dooley had this idea, this sense of action—*now, direct,
personal*—and it's filtered down to all the people who followed him, from Dr. Chaney to the newest stewardess, to
this day. It's got me—I want to do his work, and I want
to do it his way."

CHAPTER VIII

The Splendid Americans

Dr. Emmanuel Voulgaropoulos couldn't sleep. At 1 A.M. he was still watching television, though his thoughts wandered. Then the news came on and someone named Dooley began talking about his jungle hospital in Laos and his hopes to establish a second one there, and Voulgaropoulos sprang up from his chair and ran for the telephone.

He was completing his internship at a Brooklyn hospital that early spring of 1958 and wanted very badly to practice tropical medicine in some remote region where there was real need for a doctor. But he didn't want to be a missionary or a company doctor and so had been unable to find an organization within which he could do this work. Was this man Dooley his answer?

The television studio reported that the Dooley segment of the news had been filmed earlier, but that Dr. Dooley was staying at the Waldorf-Astoria Hotel. Voulgaropoulos found the number and, without regard for the late hour, promptly dialed it. And Tom Dooley, working away, also in disregard of the hour, heard what he wanted and said, "Why don't you grab a cab and come on over?"

So began a term of service for Manny Voulgaropoulos that would take him into the field for two years and keep him devoted and working for the Dooley Foundation to this day. Nor did it ever matter to him that Tom Dooley's dream sometimes outraced the realities. Told that fateful night to go to the office and tell them he was to head the Cambodia team, he went—and was met with an incredulous stare: "What team? Where's Cambodia?"

But eventually he did go, and stayed until necessity forced him to return and prepare to earn a livelihood for his young wife and baby. When TADF was organized on September 15, 1961, he was designated a director and vice president.

The following year he was participating in a newly developed program of international health studies at Johns Hopkins University and there met Dr. Narayan K. Shah, an official of the Public Health Department of Nepal. Manny's abiding interest in the Far East and Narayan Shah's deep concern for his country's awesome health problems contributed to a warm friendship between the two and they passed long hours in conversation about that landlocked Himalayan country first opened to the world little more than ten years before. Even with his long experience in Asia, Manny was appalled by the grim picture Shah painted of the disease and pestilence rampant among the Nepalese.

Pressed between India and Chinese-dominated Tibet, Nepal's 50,000 square miles include the arctic tundra of the north, studded with the fabled peaks of the Himalayas —Everest, Annapurna, Lhotse. Yet 100 miles away in the southernmost reaches, summer temperatures of 120 degrees are common and dense jungle covers the land. Roads and communications are primitive and, outside the

Kathmandu Valley, nonexistent, so that even in the capital city little was known of much of the country's 10 million population.

The bare handful of available facts was dismal indeed. One out of every two babies born in Nepal was expected to die before it reached the age of two. The people shared dark little homes with their animals and stored wheat and rice in overhead lofts crawling with weevils, rats and moles. And so isolated were they by the rugged land and the habits of the generations that whole villages had been wiped out by disease with no word reaching the next village, let alone Kathmandu, until long afterward.

Other governments have tried to help. For nearly every Embassy in Nepal there is a public works project designed to bring the twentieth century to a land that has more in common with the tenth—and to ingratiate its ideology through the medium of foreign aid. The United States assists in road building. The Soviet Union gave a modern hospital and a cigarette factory to bolster a developing tobacco industry. India has laid pipe lines for water.

And there is no question that massive infusions of government-sponsored aid are welcomed by the Nepalese leaders, for their requirements are massive. But they are a direct and open people. They have never been colonized and refuse now to become any nation's pawn. And genuinely grateful though they are for material help, they know—and have known from their first awakening to the modern world—that their most critical need is to establish a standard of health and vigor for all their people. And what government could offer that? How, in the face of incredible difficulties and unimaginable afflictions, could they even make a beginning?

One night, talking to Manny, Narayan Shah put it this

way: "We have quantitative data on only one disease, malaria. Sure, we know we have all the others you'll find in an undeveloped country—yaws, cholera, typhus, trachoma, you name it. But how they're distributed, what nutritional, climatic or parasitic factors relate to them, no one has the vaguest idea. So how can we begin establishing a rational public health program?"

And all at once Manny Voulgaropoulos thought he knew. And if he were right, if it worked, the most pressing need of the Nepalese could be met. And at least one facet of America's contribution to Nepal would stand clearly discernible from the common mass of foreign aid and would forever retain a unique identity. For it would be provided, not by the American government, but by the Thomas A. Dooley Foundation.

And this was his proposal to Shah. Suppose TADF undertook to do a complete health survey in Nepal, to evaluate its disease pathology, its nutritional and sanitation needs, to reveal for the first time how the people actually lived and what made them sick and in what numbers, so that authorities could fight back with meaningful and broadly effective public health measures. With such data in hand, the government would have a sociological as well as a medical chart of the nation—child-rearing practices and family patterns—and this, too, was essential: Nepal was a marginal country and if the infant mortality rate was to be dramatically cut without comparable gains in birth control measures, the result would be widespread famine.

Shah was instantly and passionately for the idea, yet it seemed too good to be true. "Will it work?" he asked Manny. "Will they do it?"

"I don't know," was the frank reply. "We'd both have

a lot of hard selling to do, but it's sure worth the effort, isn't it?"

And on that note they parted, Shah to present the concept to his Minister of Health and Manny to persuade Chaney that it would become TADF's most significant project. And Chaney saw it immediately. Although there would be knotty problems of funding and transportation and personnel, he had the inherent gift—as did Tom Dooley—of seeing beyond the obstacles to the ultimate meaning and effect of an enterprise, and this one caught his imagination exactly as it had Manny's and Shah's.

"Of course we'll do it," he said at once, and proceeded as though an official invitation to proceed had already been extended by His Majesty's Government. And Narayan Shah having done his work well, that was forthcoming in August, 1963, and a contract between TADF and the Nepalese Minister of Health was duly signed.

Then the difficulties began piling up. Aware that the Foundation had neither background nor personnel sufficiently trained in public health, Chaney sought an affiliation for the project with some university that had earned a solid reputation in the field. He was turned down by seven. Some couldn't spare the staff and some the money, and all spent so much time mulling over his proposal and supporting literature that a full year passed without any progress. Since a key term of the contract was that the survey be completed within three years of signing, Chaney was understandably tense as he approached his last hope, the University of Hawaii. Once again the prospects seemed bleak—there was much conversation, mostly negative, and no action—until Dr. Robert Worth of the newly organized School of Public Health expressed his unqualified enthusiasm. Worth, a forceful man in his thirties who had been born in the Far East, argued that even if proper financing failed to materialize and the actual undertaking had to be abandoned, the planning phase would be highly educational. He urged that he be allowed to take it on as a seminar for his graduate students that fall. And permission was granted.

In February, the project took another step toward reality when Shah returned to Kathmandu and began recruiting Nepalese members for the team. In Hawaii, Worth was selecting their American counterparts. And Manny Voulgaropoulos, sent to Vietnam by the State Department to devise medical programs for mountain refugees then being placed in strategic hamlets, found time to help Shah with the detailed survey plans.

Chaney was busiest of all. Having nailed down the University of Hawaii, he went after the entire state. In Honolulu, he told a press conference that the contemplated survey, in giving the government a solid base from which to work, would have a vitalizing effect on the health of the Nepalese people for generations to come, and that Hawaii, America's gateway to Asia and meeting place of East and West, ought to be specially interested. In an interview with Governor John A. Burns, he said the program could represent a unique breakthrough in foreign aid: a nongovernmental organization providing a desperately needed service for a developing nation by utilizing —assuming the people of Hawaii concurred—private funds and the resources of a single state. Invited to address the state legislature, he reported that the survey would cost $350,000, including some $80,000 for construction of a laboratory in Kathmandu; that it would take 15 months to complete; that 9,000 Nepalese in 25 villages selected at random would be given comprehensive examinations;

and that every man, woman and child in the kingdom stood to gain. "We can do this," he said. "We can go in as a private organization, no strings attached, and do the job without putting the Nepalese government on the political spot. But I need your help!"

He got it. The legislature adopted a resolution commending TADF, endorsing the survey and urging Hawaiians to pledge their support. Governor Burns declared the week of November 15–21, 1965, "Hawaiian Ambassadors to Nepal Week" and launched a campaign to have 150,-000 people donate a dollar each to the health program. The state's Senator Daniel K. Inouye and Representative Spark M. Matsunaga lauded the project on the floor of the United States Congress. Accepting appointments to head the fund-raising drive were retired Admiral Harry D. Felt, financier Chinn Ho, and Pan American's mid-Pacific manager Ernest Albrecht. Meanwhile, the Bishop Museum and the East-West Center joined the University of Hawaii in pledging technical and professional support. And somewhere along the way—no one would ever be sure just when—the Nepal health survey phased from classroom exercise to actuality.

The ten-man team included six women and arrived in Kathmandu from Hawaii in June, 1965. They were greeted by the first monsoons and spent days waiting glumly for better weather and anxiously for the arrival of their equipment. It was perhaps as well that they didn't learn of its misadventures until later: one consignment was caught in a Calcutta dock strike; another inexplicably absorbed a crate of used stewardess uniforms meant for Tibetan refugees, and when it accidentally broke open and was drenched in the endless rain, the insurance agents froze the entire shipment.

Meanwhile, Dr. Shah, overall survey director, was on hand to begin integrating Nepalese and American team members, and Bob Worth, designated project consultant, came to start them off. He had written what amounted to a scenario for the village visits, with a separate script for every person involved. But before long, like a special forces military unit, they all learned to perform at least passably in every job, should some emergency ever require it.

Then, biding time until the rains broke, they rehearsed every possible aspect of the operation in the three-acre compound that was to be Kathmandu headquarters, from setting up their portable laboratory and examination sheds to labeling specimen tubes. Passing bicyclists, pedestrians, and even the sacred cows forever wandering by, stopped to watch. Staff members of the Russian hospital just across the street gaped in amazement at the sudden activity. But if the Russians learned anything, it was certainly not that they had made a mistake by insisting that their installations be known as the Soviet Hospital. When the Aloha Medical Laboratory was completed on the survey site, the Americans made it abundantly clear that it belonged to the Nepalese people.

By early August they decided they would have to live with the monsoons. Most of the equipment had finally arrived, and Worth, who was to supervise the first field effort, yet had to be back in Hawaii for the start of the fall semester, gave the signal to move out. Target: the village of Lamatar at the edge of the Kathmandu Valley, 35 dwellings and a population of 217. The 25 test villages had been picked out of a hat, but the visitation priorities were determined by their proximity to Kathmandu.

For Nepal is a land where ground distance is measured in days and a mountain stretch that can be covered in ten minutes by air may take ten hours on foot, usually the only other feasible means of travel. And though all plans had been predicated on helicopter support—the survey would take five years to complete without it—Chaney had not yet been able to come up with one because of the demands of the war in Vietnam.

The first members of the advance team, Peyton Rowan and Captain Jal Tharpa, reached Lamatar on August 10. They were charged with maintaining equipment and establishing radio contact with Kathmandu at 8 A.M., noon, and 4 P.M. daily so that Dooley headquarters could always be sure of the field team's safety. But their main job was to pave the way for the medical team, to explain their mission, gain the people's confidence and set up camp. They were cannily chosen. Tharpa, a one-time Gurkha officer who had served 21 years with the British army, spoke the people's language and seemed to find someone in each village who had once been in his regiment. With a friend to intercede, getting the necessary permissions from the elders was considerably eased—and invariably assured when Rowan, a sanitary engineer just out of the navy, took some shots with his Polaroid camera and ten seconds later handed the astonished villagers the first pictures they had ever seen of themselves.

Next on the site were Rowan's wife Peggy, a public health nurse, and her interpreter, a sixteen-year-old Nepalese girl named Pampha Khatri Chetri. They began at once cataloguing houses, interviewing the villagers and arranging appointments for the detailed examinations and lab. tests to follow.

Three days later the medical team arrived. It was led by Dr. Virginia Singleton, who had given up a flourishing obstetrical practice in Los Angeles to work for TADF. She had spent a year at Khong Island in Laos, another in northern India with the Tibetan refugees, and now she headed the medical personnel in Nepal, all for the same $300 a month—which she donated back to the Foundation. The other team members received $150 a month and all the rice they could eat, and some of them turned the money back as well.

Dr. Singleton's interpreter was Pampha Khatri's eighteen-year-old sister Rama. Others in the group were nurse Joan Butler and jack-of-all-trades Jal Kumar Gurung. Last on the survey scene was Diane Brown, a sociologist from the University of Hawaii, who was to ferret out the practices of the local medicine men and ascertain the pregnancy and birth control patterns of the village women. Her interpreter was Manik Tuladhar, a young man who had often provided liaison for mountaineering expeditions to the Himalayas.

Back at the Kathmandu base were Dr. Shah and the survey administrative officer, Robert Murphy, who had served in the Peace Corps, and was now concerned with assuring that his far-flung colleagues were fed, supplied and transported in the face of incredible logistical difficulties. "It was," he once said, "one of those jobs that just couldn't be done. But we had to do it anyway." Rounding out the contingent were Dodie Stokes, who had worked for TADF in Cambodia and there built a hospital with her own two hands, and Carolyne McCue. They were to do all the lab. work that could not be handled in the field.

The rain continued to pound down while the team members slipped and slid through their preliminary chores. Stoically they set up tents in the camp area and stored equipment, and wet day and night, they went about their individual assignments. Peyton Rowan made a detailed map of Lamatar village showing the water sources and listing its problems of drainage and sewage. With Captain Tharpa at his side he talked to the men about their crops and made simple soil tests to see how these might be improved. This was particularly important because Lamatar is a Brahman village and the people eat neither pork nor poultry, but only goat's meat, which is expensive, and the things they grow. And though its valley is among Nepal's most fertile, the corn was small and scraggly and the people had only enough food for minimum nutrition. They knew no way to store or preserve vegetables and were totally dependent on season and weather, sometimes feasting but more often on the edge of famine.

Peggy and Pampha went from house to house, assigning each a number and listing all the occupants for later examination. They took detailed personal histories, asked about food habits and carefully noted the living conditions—neither light nor fresh air got into the windowless one-room plus loft houses; as many as fifteen people ate and slept on the dirt floors; and no one had any conception that the filth all around them bred disease.

The medical team's examinations included chest X-rays of everyone over fifteen, blood tests and urinalysis. Children were given tuberculin tests and laboratory studies searched out malaria, venereal disease, anemia and intestinal parasites.

In the two weeks they spent in Lamatar, the survey team came to know the tiny community and its people well and gained a good deal of knowledge by simple observation. For example, it was the custom for villagers to bathe each morning in the rice paddies—but that was also the place for human and animal excrement. Whenever two or more people gathered, they spent the time picking lice out of each other's hair. Skin diseases were common, as were physical deformities because of hundreds of years of intermarriage.

The Americans could also see how pathetically little it would take to improve the lot of the people materially. Soap and some clean hot water could eliminate many of the most widespread ills, but these were unknown in Lamatar, as were even the most rudimentary practices of sanitation. And, as well as medicine and medical data, the survey began to uncover the vast need for a program of health education.

The villagers, too, were frank in their curiosity about the Dooley team, for many had never seen a foreigner before. Peggy Rowan was unnerved the first morning to come out of her tent at 5 A.M. and find a sizeable crowd waiting to see what she would do next. "It was even worse," she says, "to sit down and eat while the whole village watched. I felt guilty about every mouthful—I knew the people were good and hungry—but Peyton reminded me that we alone could not solve their hunger problem and that we had to eat to work. I never did get used to it, though."

They had not come to treat illnesses either, but responded of course to emergencies and acute cases whenever they could. Sometimes, however, they had to draw the line. One man stuck his hand with a piece of bamboo and Dr. Singleton washed the superficial wound and put a Band-Aid on it. He wore it like a badge of honor and still hadn't taken it off when the survey team packed to leave ten days later. But minutes after he'd walked away from the examination shed admiring his sparkling white bandage, six others arrived to display a variety of cuts and scratches, some of them weeks old. Dr. Singleton showed them an unbandaged cut on her own hand, as bad as any of theirs, and had Rama tell them she expected to survive without a Band-Aid and that probably they would too.

On August 28, the team moved on to the second area, Pokhara, a 45-minute flight or ten days by pack train from Kathmandu—and Chaney still hadn't gotten them a helicopter. Luckily, though, Pokhara town was a zonal headquarters and so boasted an airstrip. They were able to load themselves and their gear onto a DC-3 that had been old when it flew the Hump in World War II, and then they had only to go overland 10 miles from the airstrip to the test village, Pardi Dahn. All the way, Everest, the world's mightiest mountain, loomed over their shoulders, with Annapurna dead ahead, although sometimes the soaring peaks were lost in cloud. Finished in Pokhara, they pushed on to the Bhairawa district, 55 miles south, and surveyed two more villages, then went east to Janakpur and did three more. And in the face of unbelievable obstructions, they did unbelievable things, moving equipment by elephant and cart and trudging along behind, often without choice because their food supply had been airdropped at the next village. And somehow they kept sending a flow of data back to Kathmandu.

Inevitably they ran into difficulties, too, with the people. Most were co-operative, if slightly bemused by the flurry of strangers who descended unannounced on them. But their ways were rigid and rooted in centuries-old superstitions and sometimes, all unaware, the Dooley people terrified them with perfectly innocent behavior. Once, in a village far in the west, Peggy Rowan began her household interviews sitting on the doorstep, for the late afternoon sun beat down with enervating and unrelenting fury. She completed three houses before it was time to quit for the day, then returned to her tent, had something to eat and went to bed. In the morning the three houses were gone.

For a moment Peggy thought she must have gotten turned around. But the village consisted of only a handful of dwellings and there was simply no denying the fact that three of them had disappeared, vanished, with only some well-trodden earth to show where brick walls and thatched roofs had stood. She ran to get Peyton.

"Are you sure they were the three you did yesterday?" he asked.

"Yes," she replied in awe. "Pey, it's eerie."

They found Pampha, the interpreter, and went to question the nearest neighbors. No one wanted to talk with them, or even stand long in their presence, but they persisted and at last the truth came out. These villagers regarded the pale Westerners as ghosts and wherever Peggy sat on a doorstep that ground was considered cursed and defiled. Too inherently polite to tell her this, the occupants of the three houses had had no choice but to take them down in the night and rebuild them far from the blighted places—and from the "ghost's" reach.

Peggy was appalled. "Imagine!" she said in all seriousness. "If I'd been able to start work early yesterday morning the whole village would be gone." Thereafter she conducted her interviews well away from the houses.

In another village in the South, the elders gave them permission to set up camp in the shade of two magnificently sprawling banyan trees, asking only that they not harm them as they were sacred and the site was used for certain worship services. "We had no intention of harming the trees—they were beautiful—but we sure loused up their prayer ground," Peyton says.

Unaware that the villagers were Brahmans, the Americans broiled a thick slice of buffalo meat, ate it in the cool glade—and called down the dread and consternation of all the people. Hindu priests came to march through the besmirched area, blowing horns and chanting prayers. They burned incense, made offerings of food—vegetable!—to the gods Brahma, Vishnu and Siva, and in various ways for two hours implored them to sanctify the profaned ground again.

The Dooley team had no sooner overcome that culture crisis than they verged on another. A snake crawled into the Rowans' tent and, reacting instinctively, Peyton picked up a rock and dashed its head in. When Peggy wanly reminded him that living things were sacred, he dragged it out back—making certain no one saw—and buried it. None of them was so careful, though, of the leeches and mosquitoes that beleaguered them day and night. But for every one they killed, ten more seemed to find a place on every exposed patch of skin.

In the larger villages they had a problem, too, when word spread that "American medicine men" had come and people in the countryside for miles around walked in with the plaintive hope that chronic and crippling ills could be cured in an instant by the Westerners' miraculous powers. They did whatever they could, for it was all but impossible to explain to wretchedly needful men and women that they had come to assess health requirements and were not equipped to deal with them. In some places they saw more nonsurvey patients than those designated for examination. And in Pardi Dahn, the governing council implored them to make chest X rays for a group of tuberculars from outside the village. Clearly, the prevailing notion was that the X ray itself must be beneficial, for there was no one closer than Kathmandu to whom the results could have any significance.

"How can you make them understand otherwise?" Dr. Singleton has said. "Why would we be carrying that big machine around if it couldn't cure people?"

So she made the X rays.

The most grievous difficulty remained the basic matter of getting from place to place, until at last they got their helicopter! After long negotiation, Chaney arranged to rent King Mahendra's own French Alouette, a jet-powered craft that would carry six passengers and 600 pounds of equipment. Cost: $250 per flying hour.

Around that time, two entomologists, Dr. Lawrence Quate of the Bishop Museum in Hawaii and Richard Mitchell, reported for duty, then promptly set off on a ten-week, 150-mile trek that would take them to heights of 25,000 feet and more as they sought specimens from every altitudinal range. With Sherpa guides and cases of equipment, they pushed into unknown areas, trapping 400 small mammals—rats, squirrels, weasels—and their disease-carrying parasites. Eventually these thousands of ticks, mites, lice and fleas were sent to the Bishop Museum, the University of Maryland, and the Institute for Medical Research in Malaysia for detailed laboratory analysis.

Says Quate: "We should find out a good deal about how plague and scrub typhus and the other ecto-parasitic diseases are spread. And the Nepalese public health authorities will have a clear idea of what the dangers are, and what drugs and controls are called for."

Meanwhile, with the helicopter to ease the logistical

burdens, the survey team moved steadily ahead with its testing. They came up with the idea of making a short film of their operations in the field, and this they showed in each new village as a means of introducing themselves and winning the people's confidence. Not that the work ever became routine or went off without incident or snags. The helicopter broke down and stranded them. Dr. Singleton developed osteomyelitis of the leg and had to be evacuated and replaced by Dr. Rosemarie Lanel. Then an epidemic of diarrhea swept through their camp. And once, when Chaney came to Nepal to see how things were going, Peyton Rowan told him glumly that he didn't know how they were to make the monthly payment for the helicopter rental. It totaled some $14,000 and available funds didn't come to $1,400.

"Well you just write them a check for the $14,000 anyway," Chaney said emphatically. "And if it bounces tell them to re-deposit it. I will do anything to keep this survey going—I'll get you the money somehow."

And somehow he did. And throughout the team there was suddenly a feeling that they were moving, and that despite the unimaginable problems, they were actually going to get the job done.

The first Dooley doctor in Nepal was Theodore Reich of Montreal. He had come in July, 1964, long before the health survey had emerged from the planning stage, to amass as much pertinent information as might be available in Kathmandu. There, he and Penny Watson talked with Nepalese doctors and spent endless hours extracting and collating data from medical records in a wild variety of scripts and languages. And when that work was finished, Chaney asked Reich to take over the 25-bed Dooley-supported hospital at Bharatpur in the Rapti Valley of south central Nepal.

Teddy Reich agreed, but there was a problem, a girl. She was back in Montreal, and though they had agreed to wait until his year's service with TADF was over before marrying, three weeks of separation had convinced them both that a year was barely this side of forever. There then followed a flurry of cables and they agreed to meet in Calcutta and marry at once. The problem—seemingly —was solved.

"Solved!" Wendy Reich now laughs. "That wedding of ours had more legal and theological ramifications than I'd have thought possible. *Who* was going to marry us in Calcutta?"

The Canadian consul was in New Delhi and an ordinary civil marriage would require a month's residency in India. "But I'm supposed to be working at a hospital in Nepal," Dr. Reich explained. "There are sick people there who . . ."

"It is the law."

A Hindu ceremony obviously wouldn't work, nor could the Christian churches help since Teddy was Jewish and Wendy had just become a convert. A synagogue? The rabbi was in Bombay. No one could say when he would return. The Jewish community could, of course, call together a *minyan*, a Mr. Joshua gently explained, a council of ten adult males, which would be empowered to perform the ceremony in the rabbi's absence. But they did not know these young people. How could they be certain they were in fact Jewish, or not already married? Any abetment of a sin of theirs, even unwitting, would fall on the heads of the *minyan*. Where, for example, was Wendy's conversion certificate?

"I forgot to bring it," she said miserably. "In the rush, packing . . ."

Mr. Joshua shrugged in a way that affirmed the difficulties more expressively than any words, and the forlorn couple departed.

"Nepal!" Teddy suddenly cried. "Why can't we get married in Nepal?"

They rushed pell-mell to the Nepalese consul and blurted out their question. "I am a physician working in Bharatpur," Teddy added hopefully, "and my fiancée has come all the way from Canada."

The official beamed. "You have no problem. In Nepal, when you want to get married, the girl comes from her house to your house and you are married."

"My mother would never understand," said Wendy as they left disconsolately.

"What about mine?" said Teddy.

All was not lost, however. In the morning, Mr. Joshua telephoned their hotel. He had been talking with his friends and they all felt badly about the couple's dilemma. The *minyan* would be willing to waive their other doubts and proceed with a marriage ceremony—if only they could feel certain that the young lady was really a convert. Would she be willing to go through the conversion rites again, now?

"Yes, yes!" Wendy cried. "I'm ready right now."

In an hour she had been whisked off to a nearby lake for the ritual bath. Then she was brought back to Mr. Joshua's home, where his Indian business associate's wife dressed her in a white and gold sari. The women of the Jewish community brought her flowers, and out she went to her conversion—and her wedding. Afterward, the new-lyweds were properly showered with presents and rice and escorted to their plane. And finally married and bound for her new home in Bharatpur, Wendy Reich leaned back in the seat and said, "And to think we came to Calcutta without knowing a soul."

Home turned out to be a wooden shack that had to be straightened up in the mud by a jeep with a winch and wire. But the young Reichs disinfected it, painted it, hung some curtains and decided to love it. Then Wendy, an anthropology student, started looking for a real *baidya*—a medicine man—to talk to. She found her first one when she went to a nearby village with Teddy, who was to vaccinate the people. The *baidya*, a grizzled old man without teeth, said No.

"Why not?" Teddy asked him through an interpreter. "It will keep smallpox out of your village."

"No," he said again. "I have a chicken and a drum and that is all the medicine we need."

Undaunted, Teddy took out his stethoscope and let the old man listen to the beating of his own heart. He was clearly impressed, but still unyielding. Then Teddy gave him a stimulant to sniff and told him it would make his heart beat faster, and when it did the *baidya*'s eyes snapped wide and he capitulated.

"Your medicine is the most powerful," he declared. "The people shall have it." And to make sure, he himself stood first on line, followed by his mother, three wives and his seventeen children.

Wendy Reich was properly impressed with her husband's ingenuity, but she was soon to learn that medicine in Asia is not an unbroken procession of triumphs. "The women come to the hospital holding out their babies for Teddy to see," she wrote home, "and what can he do? How many times can you talk about the starving children in this part of the world without sounding like a cliché? But here they are, little babies who look like rag dolls, slowly dying because they don't get enough to eat."

One afternoon a baby girl was brought to the hospital choking with diphtheria. The mother, a strikingly beautiful woman from the hills, hung back near the door holding the baby close while the father talked uneasily to Teddy's interpreter. The child was very sick, he said, and the *baidya* could do no more. But he had warned the parents that if they brought her to the hospital the American doctor would cut into her flesh and she would die before nightfall. "But we were afraid she would die anyway, so we came."

Teddy examined the gasping child and saw at once that he would have to perform a tracheotomy quickly or she would choke to death. When he told this to the parents, their faces blanched with fear, but they made no protest. They touched the baby's feet to their foreheads in blessing and stood silently as Teddy carried her into the operating room.

He had successfully completed the tracheotomy when, unaccountably, the child's heart stopped beating. Instantly he began breathing into her throat, a dangerous procedure, for there was no anti-diphtheria serum in the hospital. But he persisted and in a few minutes felt the little heart flutter and beat. Then it stopped again, and again he breathed life back into the racked and tormented infant. And so it went for six incredibly exhausting hours, and when Teddy Reich came out of the operating room he felt old and weary to the marrow of his bones.

"I'm sorry," he said to the mother and the father, "your baby is dead. I couldn't save her."

The mother began to sing a low mournful dirge. It echoed through the hospital and out into the compound. The father stood silent for a long time, his eyes glazed and unseeing.

"I'm sorry," Teddy said again. "Can I do anything?"

The man shook his head. There was nothing to be done, he said. They would take the child and start back for the hills at once as they had no money to stay in Bharatpur.

Teddy reached in his pocket and brought out some rupees. He started to say that it was late and that they would do better to begin their journey in the morning, but the mother struck the money from his hand, glaring savagely at him out of black eyes, and the father apologized, and together the bereaved parents wrapped their dead baby in cloth and started down the road. The woman had again taken up her piercing wail and Teddy Reich heard it for a long time after the sad couple had disappeared. And then he realized that it was just then turning dark. The *baidya* had been right after all.

The Nepal health survey, after a year and a half of brutally hard work by the Nepalese and American team members, was completed in August, 1966. A great flood of data from the villages had flowed into Dooley headquarters in Kathmandu, and from there to the analysis center at the University of Hawaii. Manny Voulgaropoulos, there to train doctors and nurses for service in underdeveloped areas, spent every spare hour helping to integrate raw facts into the cohesive health picture of a nation. Data was coded and punched out on IBM cards. Blood samples were studied, dietary habits analyzed, water supplies and sewage disposal systems evaluated. Then all the results were catalogued into three study groups of nutritional, anthropological and infectious diseases.

That winter Narayan Shah came and began writing a disease by disease summary of the Kingdom of Nepal. Included with reams of statistical data was everything that the survey team had found out about the popular belief in the causation of disease and the role of the Nepalese doctors and nurses. For public health is the point where the biological sciences and the social sciences meet: a government can start with the most comprehensive facts —and get nowhere if the people won't accept them. So it was vital for the Nepalese authorities to know where their own doctors and medical practices fit in, and where Western medicine might fit in.

All this was turned over to the Nepal Minister of Health without fuss or ceremony—and certainly with no expectation of reward. It was a gift of the Dooley Foundation, and of the people of Hawaii and the United States. Not a single tax dollar had gone into it and TADF would be a long time catching up with the money it had pledged and plunged into the effort. But the health survey was its greatest single achievement. In this gallant effort to restructure the desolate health patterns of an entire nation, to give hope to a hopeless people, the Foundation had come of age. And that was its reward.

CHAPTER IX

To Sail a Dark River

IN JANUARY, 1966, for the first time since he organized the Dooley Foundation four and a half years before, Chaney was able to pay every working member of the staff. No one will ever know the full story of his single-minded and sometimes desperate efforts in that period to keep the organization from foundering on financial rocks and sinking forever into a sea of public indifference.

On an annual budget that has never exceeded $600,000, TADF somehow maintains hospitals at Khong Island and Ban Houei Sai—both now increased to 50 beds each— the mobile X-ray unit at Pakse and the nurse-midwife training program at Khong. In Vietnam, they continue to provide assistance to Madame Ngai's An Lac orphanage. In Nepal, having completed the health survey, they have sent a technician and funds for the laboratory and for a nursing program in Kathmandu, as well as flying in short-term stewardesses on a rotating basis to teach at a Tibetan refugee nursery and a Nepalese orphanage. And in India, the two mobile health units represent the only medical care for 100,000 Tibetan refugees in the north, and the stewardesses bring to the children there the only measure of comfort and affection and education they can expect for a long time to come.

How do they do it? "We have a long history of making every penny count," Chaney says.

That history goes back to the Foundation's early days when his office was a telephone booth in the St. Francis Hotel and he would stand by it for hours waiting for a telephone call because he wanted the man at the other end to have confidence in the just-born organization. He had no concern with the trappings or whether anyone was impressed with Verne Chaney. He had found a job that needed doing and he had to do it.

If the money went out parsimoniously it came in in sometimes heartbreakingly tiny spurts. Of total cash contributions of $270,000 in 1965, for example, only a small percentage represented the grants from a few corporations and foundations. All the rest came from the intense personal efforts of the chapters, which sold Christmas cards, held cocktail parties, ran car washes, sponsored basketball games, movie premieres and moonlight boat rides. Contributions in kind—drugs, stewardess uniforms, Dooley kits of soap and face cloths—were worth another $65,000. But with some $40,000 going into travel alone— it costs more to fly to Vientiane and back than to fly around the world—TADF wound up the year $150,000 in debt.

And yet the money spent, going directly to those in need without the intervention of middlemen or power brokers, is tremendously effective. Its dollar-for-dollar value is recognized by everyone familiar with the TADF effort, from the millions in Laos and India who know that the field force is employed by no government but comes at great personal sacrifice, to men whose weight in the world is measured by their intimate knowledge of its abiding ills. Henry Cabot Lodge, who served two arduous periods as American Ambassador in Saigon, calls the Dooley people "among our most valued representatives in a tense and crucial part of Asia."

William Lederer, co-author of *The Ugly American*, that searing exposé of misspent and misdirected foreign aid in Asia, and a Dooley adherent from the very beginning, puts it this way: "Those kids came to do the job. They see, without any long lectures, what it's all about, this Dooley concept—small hospitals where they're needed, basic medicine for basic sicknesses and not the Park Avenue kind. They do what Dooley did—give the people red pills for worms and blue pills for TB and this they understand; this kind of medicine they can keep going after the Americans are gone."

One reason this private enterprise Peace Corps, financed in large part by cookie sales and car washes, has survived and now flourishes, is that its force of volunteer supporters over the land deeply believes in its goals and has never stopped working to help gain them. One is TADF Board Member Admiral Walter Moore, retired, who has fought communism in peace and war and believes the Dooley Foundation does the same job on the preventive level. "It is doing spadework in the soil of discontent and that is where communism flourishes," he says.

Sheila Kelly of the TADF New York chapter bought one of Dooley's books in the summer of 1964. She reports: "I got up from the kitchen table where I had been reading with one thought. 'If this guy's work fizzles out it's your fault and there's no doubt about it. You've heard about him. You've just read the impossible things he's accomplished. You're available to help. So help!' "

She joined the New York chapter. "Sometimes," she says, "I get a little tired of dragging shopping bags filled with things to sell or ship over to the hospitals there, especially on rainy, freezing winter nights and on some of those scorchers we have in New York in summer. But if this business takes pain away and puts a smile on some sad-eyed Dooley kid in Asia, it is absolutely my pleasure and I'm glad to go walking around New York looking like a shopping bag vendor."

Wayne McKinney worked with Dooley in Cambodia, then came home to go to medical school. "I am not trying to imitate Dr. Dooley—there can only be one like him —but I know that I have to be a jungle doctor. I keep remembering all the patients we had at Kratie, and that among the many we had to turn away because we could not physically see any more, some probably died. I was the one who had to go out and tell those sick people, some of whom had walked for days to get to the hospital, that the doctor just couldn't see any more of them because it was midnight. And so now I know I have to help out in some village somewhere or live the rest of my life with a very bad conscience."

McKinney was 34 years old when he finished his internship last summer. He left immediately for a TADF hospital in Laos.

Volunteers returning from the field provide still another valuable service—inspiration. Says Mrs. Ann Walsh Weiler of the New York chapter: "When Susan and Peter Purdy were guests at a recent meeting, there was not a dry eye in the room. Peter read letters from the children in Mussoorie thanking them and asking when they could come back, and every one of us left that meeting determined to work harder."

And stirred by Tom Dooley's own words and unquenchable courage, groups and individuals in every part of America have rallied to the support of his dream. "You must never feel," he once said, "that what I do or anyone like me does was possible because I am an extraordinary person. I am not. I'm an ordinary man. This country was founded on the idea that the ordinary man can accomplish extraordinary things."

The ordinary men and women—and youngsters—of TADF have indeed accomplished extraordinary things. They have gone to their checkbooks and piggy banks. Jean Ennis of Midlothian, Indiana, sold pencils outside Notre Dame stadium during the football season, sent $200 to San Francisco. Marie Johnson, in Thompsonville, Connecticut, got a summer job on the local paper and in lieu of salary had the editor place advertisements about the Foundation.

The Long Island chapter under the leadership of the John Churchills and the Richard Beys, have put on bingo games every Saturday evening since June 20, 1963. By early 1965 they had sent nearly $40,000 to TADF. A group of Carmel, California, artists undertook to help support the Tibetan handicraft center, shipped a steady stream of supplies to India to the refugees to perpetuate their unique crafts. In New Mexico, some oil men volunteered to send a complete well-drilling rig to Laos where water is still mainly dipped from the Mekong River and a good well is an asset beyond measure.

It is, says volunteer Elaine Reininger, a sense of involvement. "I have met so many people through the Foundation whose capacity for good exceeded what they believed about themselves. They get involved and answer the cry for help which comes, not from a neighbor across the street, but a neighbor halfway around the world, a neighbor they will never see or meet and whose personal thanks they will never know."

Chaney used to brood about the fact that TADF hospitals usually saw only the worst cases. There was a certain inevitable self-evidence about it: except for the people in Ban Houei Sai and Khong, patients had to cover great distances to get there, and so had to bring along families and animals, and for as long as they were away from home lost all their meager livelihood. And so it was hardly surprising that only the most desperately sick came. The rest, somewhere short of sound health, labored stoically on—and got sicker.

The river boats helped, but they were limited by size and carrying capacity to the relatively short stretches of the Mekong on either side of their home bases. "All you could do in the boats we had then," Chaney has said, "was pack some pills in a suitcase, take off and hope for the best. When you had one patient you had a boatload. It was a beginning, that's all."

The idea was right—to bring medical aid to the villages, to help the people while there was yet time to work a cure —if only it could be extended and expanded. And one day Chaney suddenly decided that it *had* to be extended and expanded, and on that day Project Showboat was born. On the same day he began working to bring it to life.

He envisioned a fleet of large, sturdy craft—the 40-foot houseboats so popular on American waterways, modified to carry basic medical equipment in a snug clinic, would be perfect—and he saw them plying the farthest reaches of the Mekong, between Laos and Thailand, from the China border to Cambodia, and perhaps in Vietnam as well, bringing entertainment to attract the villagers, and medicine to make them well.

Even some of his staunchest supporters said he was crazy. The expense would enormously exceed anything TADF had ever undertaken: the cost of each boat, equipped with surgical, laboratory, sterilization and X-ray facilities, together with funds sufficient to staff it and keep it operational for one year, would come to more than $100,000.

"And what if some Viet Cong or P.L. takes a shot at us?" asked an aide in the field.

"It'd be damn good publicity," Chaney said grimly. Then, "Just try not to get hit."

Raising the money was a long and incredibly frustrating task. But with the same dogged persistence that brought the Dooley Foundation to life, Chaney hammered away at the need, always the great, endless, suffering need, and slowly persuaded and promoted funds from sources as disparate as a Florida foundation ($45,000) and a San Francisco hippy (five cents). He took every penny he could get and unashamedly asked for more.

He talked himself hoarse: "If we can get out to these people on a regular basis, once a week, we can treat the sick and give the others a bar of soap and show them how to use it and to boil water—and we'll wipe out more disease than a whole boatload of penicillin."

He emphasized the need—and the promise—for training local medical aides. American personnel was to be paired with Lao or Thai people, recruited in the villages and taught to do the same medical or technical job. "You can't forever sail in and sail out without leaving some footprints behind. We don't want to keep bringing in people from West Los Angeles." And perfectly willing to use shock tactics on his audience, he usually went on, "Now I know that an American housewife would be scared stiff to be treated by someone with only six months' medical training. But we're not talking about American house-wives, or their husbands and children. We're talking about people who had no medicine before we came and will have none when we're gone except for these local aides. And they can mean the difference between life and death for millions."

Having convinced some of the shining lights of show business that the cause was worthy, he got them to go to bat for it. Arthur Godfrey told his television audience why it was called Project Showboat and why, along with medical help and the rudiments of personal hygiene, TADF planned to provide puppet shows, folk singers and free movies for the people who lived along the Mekong:

"It's rather a strange project at first glance, a team of wandering minstrels alongside of skilled surgeons and doctors floating through the middle of Asia in a houseboat. Why a showboat? Why does your doctor give your little boy a lollipop before he gives him a needle? To win him over, just as we have to win these people over, not to our politics but to our medicine. They're shy and a little scared. If we can attract their attention and give them a laugh or two we're halfway home. The greatest obstacle we face in these lands is winning the hearts and minds of simple, un-taught folk. Before we can save a child's life or even bind a wound we must overcome centuries of suspicion and apathy, ignorance and distrust. And if a guitar player helps—well, that's better than a soldier, isn't it?"

The first of the flat-bottomed, flat-topped boats was delivered early in 1967. Test-running it on a lake near Lakeport, California, Chaney turned a typical novice's mishap into a great find: he recruited the mayor of the town into TADF; Everett Owens was strolling along the lakefront that fateful date and came on the stalled houseboat. Knowing something about engines, he volunteered his help, Chaney accepted, and two hours later—with the boat now again smoothly cruising the lake—Owens found himself persuaded to accompany it to Southeast Asia as chief troubleshooter until it was finally slipped into the Mekong.

Christened *City of San Francisco*, the first showboat was shipped to Bangkok where Owens and Chaney took it in tow—literally. For the journey from Thailand to Laos was overland and arduous until, early in October, the dust-crusted boat was launched at Vientiane and run down the Mekong to the hospital dock on Khong Island. On October 21, with the *City of San Francisco* scrubbed gleaming bright again, Chaney turned the keys over to Dr. Khamphai Abhay, Minister of Health of the Royal Lao Government. Said Dr. Khamphai to the fascinated crowd: "This worthy craft is very tangible evidence of the goodwill of the American people who, knowing a need, sought to fulfill it."

Dr. Waldo Shank Jones, who took over at Khong when Mary Davia left, tells what happens when the TADF showboat heaves to at a Lao village:

"There's surprise, I suppose even shock, among the people. What's this big thing tying up to their little dock? But the music is playing and pretty soon the puppet show starts and all of a sudden they're with us."

The puppeteer is Ute Rohland, who gave up her career

as a stewardess to sign on full time with the medical minstrels. Instead of a Punch and Judy show, she tells animated stories about how boiling water kills germs and why brushing teeth is important. The dialogues are in Lao and are tape-recorded and there is little chance of anyone missing the point, for posters all over the deck demonstrate the basic principles of hygiene and sanitation.

Cartoons are shown, then public health films with a many-times magnified fly as villain. "The villagers think we have a worse health problem than they do because our flies are so much bigger," says Dr. Jones. "But all the time they're getting the message."

The show is still going on when the medical team begins immunizing the children against polio, tetanus, whooping cough and diphtheria. Each village visit ends with an opportunity for everyone to see the doctor, for the first time in nearly every case. But by the showboat's second visit, the villagers and the men and women of TADF who sail a dark river in an exotic houseboat are old friends.

The second showboat, to be called *State of Florida*, will soon be bound out for Asia and perhaps another ten are in the planning or building stage. They have proved their incalculable value. Says Dr. Jones: "Children in remote villages who once had only witch doctor medicine now have a real chance for health and normal life. And all because we have put our own magic to work—X ray and movies, inoculation and tape recorders, mircroscopes and puppets."

With mobile and expanded laboratory facilities, the floating clinic and its skilled staff can diagnose and treat maladies before they kill or cripple permanently. They have a chance—for the first time—against the classic scourges of mankind. The man with malaria can be given back his health and productivity. The child with multiple intestinal parasites can now attain a normal growth rate. Suddenly the showboats are a symbol of hope for uncounted thousands of people otherwise doomed to short life and painful death.

Says Verne Chaney: "The name showboat sounds better and better to me as I get the reports on its activities. It's turned out to be a showboat of many things—entertainment, education, medicine. But not one of the people who sail it has forgotten the thing it shows best—compassion."

Chaney sees little chance that he will ever get back to his medical practice in Monterey. The Dooley Foundation is more actively committed in Southeast Asia now than MEDICO ever was in Tom Dooley's lifetime. It is completely out of debt and slowly building up a reserve fund balance. But it continues to count on small supporters, not only for their dollars but because their sense of involvement gives meaning to the TADF credo.

It is money that provides the tangible aid—for $10 the Foundation can vaccinate 50 children against smallpox; for $15 it can free an entire household of intestinal parasites; for $25 it can provide enough antibiotics to cure fifty cases of trachoma. But it remains of first importance that each of those contributions means another person enlisted in the effort to connect East and West, man and man.

As for the Dooley volunteers, past and present they now number into the many hundreds. And each one, in his way, in a world of computers and nuclear weaponry and impersonal technology, has answered the question: What can one person do?

Each year, TADF honors the public figures who have most contributed to humanitarian endeavor internationally. Its Splendid American awards have gone to Ambassador Henry Cabot Lodge, Secretary of State Dean Rusk, Bob Hope, former Ambassador to Japan Edwin O. Reischauer, Danny Kaye, Senator Daniel K. Inouye and Kirk Douglas. The presentations are made at a gala black-tie dinner party with appropriate speeches, entertainment and, at $50 a plate, a handsome boost to Foundation finances.

And while the award winners are properly lauded for their service, they themselves are quick to take public notice of the fact that TADF's most splendid Americans almost never get to the party, for they are the men and women in the field. Yet they are what the party is really all about and they are always there in spirit. They have met the simple requirements for service that Tom Dooley envisioned ten years ago, and they have given life to his dream.

"We are in no way a religious or political organization," Dooley once said. "We believe we can win the friendship of people only by working beside them, humans-to-humans, toward goals they understand and seek themselves. Our instrument for this shall be medicine."

About the Author

LAWRENCE ELLIOTT was born in Brooklyn and is a graduate of the City College of New York. He began writing professionally twenty years ago. Although he has contributed to a wide range of magazines, he has been most closely associated with the *Reader's Digest* and, since 1959, has written some forty articles for them. From 1960 until last year, he covered Alaska and western Canada for the *Digest* and is currently assigned to their European Editorial Office in Paris. Mr. Elliott has three young daughters and is an avid collector of modern American first editions. His other books are *A Little Girl's Gift* (1963); *George Washington Carver: The Man Who Overcame* (1966); *On the Edge of Nowhere* (with James Huntington, 1966); and *Journey to Washington* (with Senator Daniel K. Inouye, 1967).